Making Sense of Psychiatric Diagnosis

Understanding the DSM-5

Ashley L Peterson RN BSN BScPharm MPN

With Guest Contributors

MH@H
Books

Mental Health @ Home Books

This book is intended to provide general knowledge, and is not intended to diagnose or serve as medical advice of any sort. There is no substitute for an assessment and diagnosis by a qualified health professional.

While this book describes the content of the DSM-5, it does not represent, nor is it a substitute for, the exact diagnostic criteria included in the DSM-5.

The information in this book is correct to the best of the author's knowledge at the time of publication. The author is not responsible for any errors or omissions, and makes no warranty in regards to the contents of this book.

Published by Mental Health @ Home Books.
mentalhealthathome.org
ISBN 978-1-9990008-2-0

Contributors

These are the amazing contributors who have helped to make this book happen by sharing their first-hand experiences of mental illness. A huge thank you to all of them!

Alexis Rose (PTSD)
Untangled: https://atribeuntangled.com/

Alice Franklin (Tourette's)
How to Have Tourette's: https://how-to-have-tourettes-syndrome.com/

Autumn Skies Blog (social anxiety disorder)
AutumnSkiesBlog: autumnskiesblog.wordpress.com

Beckie (body focused repetitive behaviour disorder)
Beckie's Mental Mess: http://beckiesmentalmess.blog/

Candace (alcohol use disorder)
Revenge of Eve: https://revengeofeve.com

Casey Elizabeth Dennis (ADHD)
This Bipolar Brat: https://bipolarbrat.wordpress.com/

Caz (bulimia nervosa)
Invisibly Me: www.invisiblyme.com

Christina (generalized anxiety disorder)
Sea of Words: https://seaofwordsx.wordpress.com/

Elle Rose (depersonalization/derealization disorder)
Secretladyspider: https://secretladyspider.wordpress.com/

Johnzelle Anderson (panic disorder)
Panoramic Counseling: PanoramicCounseling.com

Katie Dale (bipolar I disorder)
Bipolar Brave: https://bipolarbrave.com

Katie (OCD, somatic symptom-related disorder)
Let's Talk Anxiety Disorders and Depression:
https://letstalkanxietyanddepression540391349.wordpress.com

Luftmentsch (autism spectrum disorder)
Vision of the Night: https://visionofthenight.wordpress.com/

Meg Kimball (schizophrenia)
Why does bad advice happen to good people?
https://whenbadadvicehappens.wordpress.com/

Noha Nova (schizoaffective disorder)
Schizoaffective Disorder and My Life: https://ramblingsofaschizomind.wordpress.com/

Paula Light, Light Motifs II (anorexia nervosa)
Light Motifs II: https://lightmotifs.wordpress.com/

Phyllis Engle (bipolar II disorder)
Color Me Bipolar: https://colormebipolar.wordpress.com/

Wonderfull Creature (borderline personality disorder)
Mental Illness Worrior: http://emotionalillnessworrior.wordpress.com/

Table of Contents

Introduction   **1**

Diagnostic Systems   **4**

Anxiety Disorders   **14**

Social Anxiety Disorder (Social Phobia)   15

Autumn Skies Blog's Story (Social Anxiety Disorder)   *17*

Panic Disorder   18

Johnzelle's Story (Panic Disorder)   *21*

Generalized Anxiety Disorder (GAD)   22

Christina's Story (Generalized Anxiety Disorder)   *24*

Bipolar and Related Disorders   **26**

Bipolar I Disorder   33

Katie's Story (Bipolar I)   *35*

Bipolar II Disorder   36

Phyllis's Story (Bipolar II)   *37*

Cyclothymic Disorder   39

Depressive Disorders   **41**

Major Depressive Disorder (MDD)   41

Ashley's Story (Major Depressive Disorder)   *47*

Persistent Depressive Disorder (Dysthymia)   48

Dissociative Disorders   **50**

Dissociative Identity Disorder (DID)   50

Depersonalization/Derealization Disorder (DPDR)   52

Elle Rose's Story (Depersonalization/Derealization Disorder)   *54*

Feeding and Eating Disorders   **55**

Anorexia Nervosa   55

Paula's Story (Anorexia Nervosa)   *57*

Bulimia Nervosa   58

Caz's Story (Bulimia Nervosa)   *60*

Gender Dysphoria   **62**

Neurodevelopmental Disorders   **65**

Attention-Deficit/Hyperactivity Disorder (ADHD)   65

Casey's Story (ADHD)   *68*

Autism Spectrum Disorder   70

Luftmentsch's Story (Autism Spectrum Disorder)   *72*

Tic Disorders: Tourette's Disorder   74

Alice's Story (Tourette's Disorder)   *75*

OCD and Related Disorders   **77**

Obsessive Compulsive Disorder (OCD)   77

Katie's Story (OCD)   *79*

Body Dysmorphic Disorder   81

Trichotillomania and Other Body-Focused Repetitive Behaviour Disorders   82

Beckie's Story (Body-Focused Repetitive Behaviour Disorder)   *84*

Personality Disorders   **86**

Borderline Personality Disorder (BPD)   88

Wonderfull Creature's Story (BPD)   *91*

Narcissistic Personality Disorder (NPD)   92

Psychotic Disorders   **95**

Delusional Disorder   98

Schizophrenia   100

Meg's Story (Schizophrenia)   *104*

Schizoaffective Disorder   105

Noha Nova's Story   *106*

(Schizoaffective Disorder)   *106*

Somatic Symptom and Related Disorders   **108**

Somatic Symptom Disorder   108

Illness Anxiety Disorder   110

Katie's Story (Somatic Symptom-Related Disorder)   *112*

Substance Use Disorders   **114**

Alcohol Use Disorder   115

Candace's Story (Alcohol Use Disorder)   *117*

Gambling Disorder   118

Trauma and Stressor-Related Disorders   **121**

Posttraumatic Stress Disorder (PTSD)   121

Alexis Rose's Story (PTSD)   *126*

Adjustment Disorders   127

The Diagnosis Experience: Interviews Round #1   **130**

Correcting Misinformation: Interviews Round #2   **136**

What Diagnosis Means for Recovery: Interviews Round #3   **141**

The Evolving Nature of Diagnosis   **146**

Contributor Biographies   **148**

Author Biography   **150**

Introduction

A diagnosis may be just a label, but it's a label that can have profound consequences for the person it's applied to, affecting identity, access to mental health services, perception by others, and stigma. This book will help you to gain a better understanding of what's actually involved in a wide variety of mental illnesses and the diagnostic labels that are attached to them. While much of the book includes language like "we" and "us" to refer to those of us living with mental illness, the reader who doesn't have a mental illness is just as welcome in this conversation.

A diagnostic label is not something that is voluntarily chosen; instead, it's something that others in a position of authority decide whether or not to apply. That lack of control can be challenging, especially since a diagnosis can end up having a profound impact on personal identity. While there may be limited control over the diagnosis given, everyone has the right to know what they've been diagnosed with and why. Getting a diagnosis can be a good starting point for learning more about the condition(s) and its symptoms, and it can be a springboard in the journey towards wellness.

This book is based on diagnostic criteria from the Diagnostic and Statistical Manual of Mental Disorders 5th edition (DSM-5), and presents the diagnostic criteria in paraphrased and/or summarized form. Not every diagnosis will be covered; instead, the aim is to give a representative overview of a variety of different types of illnesses. The chapters in this book are based on the diagnostic groupings in the DSM-5, and the diagnosis chapters are laid out in alphabetical order by title.

For each disorder, the diagnostic criteria information is interspersed with additional commentary. Direct quotes are used where paraphrasing seemed unlikely to be able to effectively capture the message. The criteria described refer to diagnosis in adults. Some conditions have minor variations in criteria when making a diagnosis in children and adolescents, but those are not included here.

Interspersed with the diagnostic criteria are additional explanations in order to provide greater clarity regarding each symptom. These explanations incorporate several sources of information. One is the detailed information included in each DSM chapter; in the DSM-5, the diagnostic criteria for each illness is followed by an often lengthy explanation of the symptoms as well as information about age of onset, gender prevalence, and typical course of illness. This book also draws on my years of education and experience as a mental health nurse, and my own experience living with major depressive disorder provides additional context.

The terminology used in this book reflects the standard terms used in the DSM-5, along with other terms commonly used in the field of psychiatry. It's much more useful to describe mental illness using clearly defined language rather than colloquial terms that have inexact, imprecise meanings. In some chapters commonly used colloquial terms will be discussed, along with their relationship to diagnostic terminology.

"High functioning" is a term that's often used casually to refer to people who have a mental illness of some sort but are still able to maintain a reasonably intact level of daily functioning. "High functioning" is not a DSM-5 term, nor is it frequently used in the field of psychiatry. Whether someone is referred to as high functioning or not, they must meet the same diagnostic criteria as anyone else to receive a diagnosis.

This book is not intended in any way to diagnose or to provide any form of medical advice, and is written for informational purposes only. It can be very tempting to self-diagnose, but in the next chapter you'll see why that really doesn't work well the vast majority of the time. However, knowing the diagnostic criteria for an illness can provide a framework for understanding which particular experiences are likely to be reflective of illness and which are not.

Throughout the book I use "normal" in quotations to refer to people who are not mentally ill, or to thoughts/emotions that are not representative of illness (e.g. it is "normal" to feel sad during the grieving process). I also use "normal" to distinguish between what someone might experience when they're relatively well and what they experience when ill. The use of the term normal is not intended to imply in any way that those of us with mental illness are any more or less normal/abnormal overall than anyone else; it's simply a term that's convenient in its brevity.

The term "patient" is sometimes used to refer to the particular role that's filled when interacting with a mental health care provider. This is not intended to imply that patient, or mentally ill for that matter, are the only roles that people play, or the most important roles that they fulfill in their mental illness journey. However, in the context of receiving a diagnosis that role descriptor seems appropriate.

Many of the diagnoses described in this book are accompanied by a firsthand narrative written by someone who lives with that disorder. The voices of the writers who have contributed to this book add tremendous richness, bringing the symptom criteria to life. When they came on board with this project, I told each of them that I was looking for a "feels like" story, with the aim of giving you as a reader an idea of what it feels like to have each of the mental illnesses described in this book. They have most certainly delivered.

Just as each human being is unique, each individual living with a particular illness is unique. These narratives do not represent the only way of experiencing an illness, but they give you a genuine, profoundly human look at the reality of these illnesses.

Because many of the contributors had more they wanted to say than the narratives included in the diagnosis chapters, there are three chapters at the end of the book devoted to interview-style questions, with answers from contributors representing various diagnosis. There is a great deal of commonality shown in the contributors' answers, regardless of diagnosis.

I'm so grateful to each of the contributors for getting on board with this project. They are all excellent writers and advocates. Their names and blog details are listed on the contributor list at the beginning of this book. It's truly been a privilege to have each of them involved.

Diagnostic Systems

Diagnosis is only meaningful if everyone is talking about the same thing, comparing apples to apples. Diagnostic standards are required for any form of illness, whether mental and physical, in order to achieve consistency and clinical relevance. While a diagnosis will never be able to give a complete picture of any specific individual and their experiences, it's an important way of communicating amongst healthcare providers so that everyone's on the same page, or at the very least on the same chapter.

There are two main diagnostic systems used in the diagnosis of mental illness. The American Psychiatric Association publishes the Diagnostic and Statistical Manual of Mental Disorders (DSM), which is currently in its 5th edition. The other major system is the World Health Organization's International Classification of Diseases (ICD), now in its 11th edition. The ICD includes both physical and mental health disorders, while the DSM contains only mental illnesses. The ICD is quite similar to the DSM, although there are some differences; for example, the ICD-11 considers complex PTSD to be a distinct diagnosis from regular PTSD, while the DSM-5 considers them to be covered by the single diagnosis of PTSD.

With every new edition of these manuals that's published, the diagnostic systems continue to evolve. For each new edition of the DSM, the APA puts together committees of experts, with working groups devoted to specific clusters of diagnoses. In the years that it takes to put together a new edition, diagnoses from the previous edition are reviewed and revised as needed, and new diagnoses are considered for inclusion. Some changes between editions are relatively minor, while others are more significant. Of course, what the people with these illnesses are actually experiencing isn't changing; it's the diagnostic constructs that are adapting to (hopefully) better capture the experiences of people with mental illnesses. The diagnostic constructs themselves are fallible, as are the people who develop them, but that doesn't make the illnesses they're describing any less real or valid. There will inevitably be both strengths and weaknesses in any diagnostic system.

The current version of the DSM, the DSM-5, was released in 2013. The previous edition was the DSM-IV-TR (text revision). The DSM-5 marked a shift away from roman numerals for designating the edition number; this was done in order to appear more modern.

One notable change was a shift away from the multi-axial system for putting together a diagnostic formulation. The DSM-IV used a 5-axis system to attempt to capture the full clinical picture of an individual's condition. Axis I included major mental disorders, axis II was for personality and developmental disorders, axis III was for physical health conditions, axis IV covered major psychosocial stressors, and axis V was a global assessment of functioning, based on a 1-100 scale. That system is no longer used in the DSM-5. Other changes include removing the bereavement exclusion from the diagnostic criteria for a major depressive episode, reworking the symptom clusters for the diagnosis of PTSD, and doing away with the distinction between substance abuse and dependence, replacing them with the single diagnosis of [substance] use disorder.

The "statistical" part of the DSM's name comes into play in deciding how many symptom criteria a person must meet in order to be given a diagnosis. For example, if a person needs to meet 4 out of 6 criteria to be diagnosed with condition X, it's because the number crunching seems to show that 4 symptoms is where you see a clear separation between "normal" people and people with the illness. There is a fine balance between wanting the bar set high enough that "normal" people don't get diagnosed as ill, but also low enough to make sure that most of the people who are actually ill do meet the criteria for diagnosis. Yes, there is inherently some degree of arbitrariness, but at the same time I'm not sure what a better alternative would be.

Unlike many medical diagnoses, there are no specific diagnostic tests like bloodwork or imaging studies that can diagnose mental illness. Certain changes visible on imaging tests may be seen more often in people with particular illnesses, but nothing has yet been identified that is specific enough to reliably differentiate ill from not ill. Diagnosis, therefore, is based on a thorough clinical evaluation and history-taking. Because of the subjectivity that's inherent in this process, it's entirely possible that two clinicians could evaluate the same patient and conclude that different diagnoses were responsible for the symptoms. Diagnostic accuracy depends to a large extent on the interviewing and history-taking skill of the clinician, and their ability to elicit key information from the patient and other relevant sources.

It's also worth keeping in mind that insurance billing relies on diagnostic codes. There are numerical codes assigned to each diagnosis in the DSM and the ICD, and it is based on these codes that health care providers are generally paid. This opens up at least the possibility that some providers may be biased towards assigning a diagnosis to a patient who might be right on the borderline of meeting the criteria for a given diagnosis. Whether this does or does not actually happen in practice, it's a potential downside inherent in diagnostic code-based compensation for healthcare professionals.

Ashley L Peterson

How to Use the DSM

To a casual reader, the DSM may seem kind of like a cookbook – if you have enough symptom ingredients then you've got yourself a diagnosis. However, the DSM was never intended to be used that way, a point that it addresses explicitly.

Many of the symptoms in the DSM represent a variation of experiences that "normal" people have some of the time, to some extent. Based on that, it would be easy to conclude that almost everyone meets the criteria for one or more of the diagnoses in the DSM. What's missing from that equation, though, is the years of education and clinical experience that give a clinician a broad enough information base to differentiate between "normal" and pathological. In their training, health care professionals are exposed to an array of different patients with various mental health conditions of differing severities. They learn what mentally ill "looks like", not in the sense of outward appearance, but rather they see how the symptoms actually tend to manifest in individuals experiencing the illness, and the range of different ways the illness can present. To differentiate between "normal" and pathological, one needs to have an appropriate frame of reference and the clinical judgment to make a proper evaluation, and the average person without clinical training simply doesn't have that.

Only certain professions have the formal authority to make psychiatric diagnoses within their scope of practice, and this is dependent on the professional regulations in a given area. Medical doctors, including psychiatrists, are able to make psychiatric as well as other medical diagnoses. The same is true for nurse practitioners. Clinical psychologists and clinical social workers can often make psychiatric diagnoses, although this may not be the case in all areas. In this book, the generic term clinician is used to refer to any mental health professional who is qualified to make psychiatric diagnoses.

When a patient presents with symptoms that don't clearly fit into any specific diagnosis, they may be given a diagnosis of unspecified [x] disorder, e.g. unspecified depressive disorder. In the DSM-IV, this was referred to as depressive disorder not otherwise specified (NOS). While this may at first glance seem rather vague, just because someone doesn't fit into a neat diagnostic box doesn't mean they're not ill, and the unspecified label helps to capture that. It should be used to make sure ill people who otherwise might not fit a diagnostic code can be directed towards appropriate treatment, not as an excuse to slap a diagnostic label on someone who's not actually ill.

A set of diagnostic criteria do not paint a precise picture of what that particular illness *must* look like in all people with the diagnosis. For most diagnoses there are a certain minimum number of criteria that a person must meet, but exactly which symptoms they have and how those symptoms present themselves can vary widely from one individual to the next, and also from one point in time to another. Two people might have the same diagnosis but quite a

6

different mix of symptoms, so a diagnosis alone is not enough to give a clear understanding of a specific individual's illness experience.

A diagnosis serves as an explanation for symptoms. It does not change who or what a diagnosed person is. Because diagnoses are human constructs, they are susceptible to change. Sometimes changes are made because a new provider has a different interpretation of the overall symptom picture. Other times, new symptoms will become apparent as the illness evolves that require a revision of the diagnosis. As will be explained in a subsequent chapter, this is not uncommon in individuals with bipolar II, who may be initially be diagnosed with major depressive disorder because they don't have a recognized hypomanic episode until after one or more episodes of depression.

Perhaps at some point in the future we will have a better understanding of the biological basis of illness, and more objective diagnostic standards will be determined. We're not there yet, though, so in the meantime a subjective approach to diagnosis is the best we've got.

❄ ❄ ❄

Differential Diagnosis

Diagnosis is not always cut and dried, and the same symptom can potentially occur in multiple different DSM disorders. The term "differential diagnosis" refers to the process of determining the potential diagnoses that could account for the symptoms the individual is experiencing. The clinician will then try to narrow that down to come up with the diagnosis that best fits the overall symptom presentation. Sometimes this can be quite challenging, and it may take time to gather information to formulate a clear diagnosis.

If a clinician suspects one disorder but is unable to totally exclude another as a possibility, the diagnostic formulation may include "rule out [disorder X]". This means that additional information needs to be gathered from other sources or additional observation/assessment in order to be certain of whether or not the person might meet the criteria for the diagnosis.

Personality disorders may initially be listed in the diagnosis as a "rule out" because they can require a longer period of assessment to be clear on the diagnosis. If a patient has been seeing the same clinician for an extended period of time, there generally shouldn't be any lingering "rule outs" left over from the initial assessment that haven't been resolved.

All of the diagnoses in the DSM-5 have criteria that involve ruling out either a medical condition or a drug as the cause of the presenting symptoms. Certain physical health conditions, including brain disorders, can produce symptoms that mimic psychiatric illness. Psychiatrists have general medical training, and part of the history-taking process involves identifying any symptoms which require further medical consultation. In some cases, making a psychiatric diagnosis may need to be deferred until further medical examination is done to rule out potential medical causes.

There are multiple substances, ranging from prescription medications to street drugs, that can trigger psychiatric symptoms. While street drugs may jump to mind as an obvious possibility, it's important not to overlook the role that prescribed medications can potentially play. If someone experiences depressive, manic, or psychotic symptoms solely as a result of something they have put into their body, the diagnosis should reflect that rather than an underlying mood or psychotic disorder. Sometimes this is quickly apparent, while in other cases a much closer investigation is required. It's also possible for a medication or street drug to unmask a mental illness that was already brewing under the surface.

Here is just a small sample of medications that can cause psychiatric symptoms:

Depression:
- alcohol
- benzodiazepines
- calcium channel blockers (cardiac/blood pressure medication)
- certain antivirals and antibiotics
- steroids

Mania:
- alcohol
- cyclobenzaprine (muscle relaxant)
- dextromethorphan (cough suppressant)
- steroids
- certain heart medications

Psychosis:
- certain antivirals
- certain heart medications
- NSAIDs (anti-inflammatories)
- steroids

It's not unusual for people to accumulate multiple psychiatric diagnoses. Sometimes this is because there are legitimately multiple different co-occurring conditions. Other times, it can result from diagnoses being made at different points in time by different clinicians. Most DSM-5 diagnoses include a criterion that the symptoms must not be better accounted for by another mental illness. If there is a single diagnosis that best explains a cluster of symptoms, it's probably not appropriate to add an additional diagnosis.

If a new diagnosis becomes apparent and it better explains symptoms that were previously attributed to another diagnosis, the previous diagnosis should most likely be axed. Sometimes by meeting the criteria for a new diagnosis, someone will no longer pass the "rule out" criteria of the original diagnosis. For example, someone can't simultaneously be diagnosed with bipolar disorder and major depressive disorder, since the two are mutually exclusive based on their diagnostic criteria.

Sometimes people will self-identify as having multiple diagnoses when in fact all of those elements fall under the umbrella of a single diagnosis. For example, someone who identifies as having bipolar disorder, depression, and seasonal affective disorder probably doesn't actually have three diagnoses; their diagnosis would be bipolar disorder with seasonal pattern.

The more identified diagnoses a person has, the more useful it is to do a sort of diagnostic spring cleaning every so often with the treatment team to clarify that the diagnoses are the right fit for the current clinical picture. It's possible that there could be some spare ones kicking around that are no longer serving a meaningful purpose.

❅ ❅ ❅

Why Self-Diagnosis Doesn't Work

Whenever we ourselves are struggling, or we see people around us having difficulties, the natural tendency is to try to understand the reason for it. This can sometimes lead people to turn to the DSM to look for a diagnosis that would explain the problems. While doing so may feel reassuring, chances are it's not particularly accurate. That's not to say that someone needs to have a formal diagnosis in order to have a valid mental illness, but it's hard to make an objective evaluation when we're in the midst of something.

One issue is that many mental illnesses by their very nature impair the insight that people have into their condition, making it difficult to gain perspective. "Anosognosia" is the medical term for this lack of insight. In particular, psychosis and mania can skew the ability to accurately evaluate one's own experiences. Sometimes, symptoms are not seen as being subjectively distressing, making it difficult for the person to recognize that what they're experiencing is due to illness. For example, people with bipolar II disorder may identify as having depression but not see anything problematic about their hypomanic symptoms. People with depression may blame their own personal flaws or weaknesses for what they are experiencing rather than attributing the symptoms to illness.

Determining whether a symptom is pathological in nature or in magnitude requires an appropriate frame of reference for comparison. Mental health professionals have seen a large number of patients with symptoms ranging from mild to severe, so they're able to compare the symptoms they observe in a specific patient to that broad range. For most people who might be trying to self-diagnose, their frame of reference is far more limited, so they're not in a good position to accurately evaluate what they're experiencing in a bigger picture sense.

You'll notice that most of the diagnoses covered in this book include the criterion "clinically significant distress or impairment in social, occupational, or other important areas of functioning," or some variation thereof. While this may not sound particularly meaningful, it's actually an important part of distinguishing "normal" experience from illness. Again, this requires an appropriate frame of reference that's developed through clinical training, and most people considering self-diagnosis haven't had the opportunity to develop this.

For many diagnoses, and particularly for personality disorders, it's important to look at the pattern of symptoms over time. This is very hard for us to do for ourselves in any sort of objective way; we're far too close to the trees to be able to see the forest. Often it's useful to have other people's input to help the clinician to establish a clear history. This is why health professionals will often look for "collateral" information from other sources. It's not because the patient isn't believable, but rather because getting somewhat more objective input helps to paint a clearer overall picture.

However, clinicians need to recognize that family members are often pretty close up to the trees as well, and they may not have a great view of the forest either. If what the family members are saying doesn't fit with what the clinician is picking up when interviewing the patient, the clinician needs to figure out why that might be. Family members can sometimes have their own agendas, and the clinician needs to critically evaluate the information they're being given. Collateral information gained from family members should not be treated as gospel. Rather, it should be used as part of a triangulation process that's used to get the broadest possible picture. The clearer the picture is, the stronger the diagnostic certainty.

All of that being said, there are cases where, for whatever reasons, people who are experiencing symptoms of mental illness are unable to get an effective assessment done. That lack of effective assessment may be due to lack of access to clinicians who are appropriately trained in the particular illness in question, or it may be that during the assessment interview(s) the clinician feels they've been unable to gather sufficient information to support making a diagnosis. This book includes a narrative by someone who has had difficulty accessing effective assessment for autism for a number of reasons, and he provides an excellent example of how the lack of formal diagnosis doesn't detract from the illness experience that someone may be having.

❈ ❈ ❈

What a Diagnosis Should Do

Diagnosis can serve a number of purposes. As previously mentioned, diagnostic codes are used for insurance billing purposes. Mental health services generally have inclusion and exclusion criteria that are based on diagnosis, so a particular diagnosis or combination of diagnoses can potentially open the door or slam it shut in your face.

Diagnosis/diagnoses and other information in someone's medical record are an important way to communicate between different health professionals. That is often a good thing, but it can also mean that a misdiagnosis may end up following you around. There's no way to remove inaccurate diagnoses entirely from your record, because that represented that clinician's medical opinion at that point in time, and going back and changing medical records is not legally permitted. While that can be frustrating, if you think about it, allowing clinicians to go back and make changes to medical records wouldn't really be a good thing. If something bad were to happen to you, you certainly wouldn't want health professionals going back and changing their charting to cover their butts. In the case of incorrect diagnoses, probably the most workable option will be for your current clinician to clearly state in some form of case review note why they don't think the previous diagnosis is appropriate/applicable.

Stigma is often linked to labels, so having a mental illness label may make someone more of a target for stereotyped attitudes and discriminatory behaviours. This has far less to do with the illness itself and more to do with societal misconceptions. While it may be easy to focus on the label itself as the target of stigma, the label is merely an easy thing for people to latch on to; the fears and the prejudice are really focused on the observable illness-related behaviours associated with stereotypes, and assumptions and underlying beliefs about what the illness and its associated behaviours represent.

Having a diagnostic label can be helpful in finding a community of other people who have been through similar experiences. This kind of illness-focused community-building can be very helpful in addressing self-stigma. It allows a shift from a feeling of out-group in the context of broader society to a feeling of in-group related to others within the illness community.

Diagnosis is most useful when it aids in understanding illness-related experiences and/or points the way toward effective treatment. Having a diagnosis may help to validate what someone is experiencing, and it may help to normalize that experience as something that also affects other people in similar ways. Regardless of the diagnostic label, the symptoms pre-diagnosis are still the same symptoms post-diagnosis. The illness itself is the same, with or without a diagnostic label attached.

Whether or not you choose to incorporate your illness into your core identity is totally up to you. That's also something that may change over the course of time as your illness evolves and perhaps becomes more chronic in nature. Regardless, you are not reducible as a person to your mental illness alone, nor does your illness define your inherent worth.

❉ ❉ ❉

Flaws in the System

The DSM is not perfect by any stretch of the imagination. Previous editions have included things that would be viewed as absurd now, such as listing homosexuality as a mental illness. Decisions on what diagnoses to include and the criteria for those diagnoses are arrived at based on committees that tend to be stacked heavily with wealthy older white men. However, that doesn't mean we need to toss the baby out with the bathwater and write off the entire DSM.

With the current state of scientific knowledge, there are no known biological tests or markers that firmly establish a mental illness diagnosis, so the only way to make a diagnosis is based on subjective criteria. Psychiatric diagnoses are constructs that people have developed to try to capture certain clusters of symptoms. It's not that the conditions aren't real, but at this point psychiatric diagnoses are labels that capture groups of observed symptoms rather than specify exactly what is going wrong in the brain. This is far from perfect, but right now it's the best we can do. The fact that the diagnostic system isn't ideal does not detract from the very real distress experienced by people living with these illnesses.

It's also worth differentiating between problems with the DSM-5 as a diagnostic manual and problems with how some clinicians may be using it. If overworked and underpaid primary care physicians are potentially over-diagnosing "normal" complaints as major depression or anxiety disorders, that's not necessarily a flaw with the DSM itself. It may have more to do with systemic issues, like getting paid for the visit and writing a prescription because talk therapy is not available in a timely, affordable manner. Attributing these sorts of system-related effects to problems with the DSM itself ends up taking attention away from fundamental problems within the healthcare system that need to be addressed.

Some problems in diagnostic accuracy and precision may be system-related, but others relate more to clinical skill. Since psychiatric diagnosis is subjective, accurate diagnosis depends on a clinician's ability to gather as much relevant information from the patient as they can. A clinician may have a great deal of knowledge about mental illness, but if they're unable to effectively establish rapport with a patient, the patient may not feel comfortable disclosing crucial information. The accuracy of the diagnosis is thus limited by the clinician's poor interviewing skills. Stigma can also come into play here; a clinician may not realize that they're conveying stigma-laden messages, and the patient may respond by shutting down and limiting their responses. This problem is indirectly related to the subjectivity of the DSM, but the fundamental problem here is with professional competence rather than the DSM itself.

On the other hand, even a highly skilled clinician may be unable to elicit all of the relevant information due to factors on the patient's side. The patient may have had previous negative experiences with treatment providers, making them reluctant to disclose information. A history of trauma can make it difficult to trust others. The symptoms of the illness itself may make it very difficult for the patient to recall and effectively explain relevant information.

Despite the flaws, at this point there isn't a better alternative, so we must make the best of what we've got. Now that we've got those preliminaries out of the way, it's time to move on to the specific diagnoses.

Anxiety Disorders

Anxiety and worry are normal emotions, which come with associated thoughts, that everyone is likely to experience every so often. However, feeling emotionally anxious is very different from having an anxiety disorder. It's rather unfortunate that the emotion and the illness are represented by the same word, as it can make it easier for the uninformed to dismiss anxiety disorders as being "just" anxiety.

Anxiety disorders often cause as many physical symptoms as they do mental symptoms. The body's fight-or-flight response can be activated, which affects things like heart rate and breathing patterns. These physical symptoms of anxiety may lead sufferers to think they are experiencing physical health emergencies. If someone presents to the emergency department with these types of symptoms and a physical cause is ruled out, that person might be unfortunate enough to be told "it's all in your head" or "it's just anxiety", neither of which is the least bit helpful. After all, what's inside the head is the brain, which is by far the most complex and powerful organ in the human body.

This chapter covers social anxiety disorder, panic disorder, and generalized anxiety disorder. Other anxiety disorders listed in the DSM-5 include selective mutism, specific phobias (i.e. phobias about specific things), and agoraphobia.

Before moving on to the anxiety disorder diagnoses, it's worth clarifying a few terms related to anxiety and panic:

- **Fear:** Fear is associated with immediate danger and activation of the nervous system's fight or flight response. Panic disorder involves abnormal fear responses.

- **Anxiety**: This arises from anticipation of a future threat, and involves emotional, cognitive, and physical elements.

- **Worry**: Worry is an apprehensive expectation that is more cognitively-based than anxiety is, and tends to be focused around a particular situation.

Social Anxiety Disorder (Social Phobia)

This anxiety disorder focuses specifically on social interactions with others, and the key feature is the expectation of negative evaluation, humiliation, and rejection in social situations.

The criteria for social anxiety disorder are:

✦ *There is a marked fear of social situations where there is the potential for scrutiny by others.*

> This criterion narrows the focus to situations where one might expect to be scrutinized by other people, so spending time at home with family or a significant other may be much easier to manage.

✦ *There is a fear of acting in a way that will be judged as negative by others.*

> The fear of negative evaluations may relate to being perceived as weak, crazy, unintelligent, uninteresting., or other negative judgments. The individual may be highly preoccupied with concerns that their physical signs of anxiety, such as tremor, may be obvious to others and bring about further negative judgments, embarrassment, and humiliation.

✦ *These types of social situations trigger fear and anxiety nearly all of the time.*

> The symptoms are experienced across almost all social situations on a consistent basis. The length of time experiencing anticipatory anxiety leading up to social occasions may vary, and can begin far in advance of the event itself.

✦ *These social situations are either avoided or handled with significant fear/ anxiety.*

> Significant measures may be taken to avoid social situations if at all possible. It likely won't be possible to avoid social situations entirely as a person might wish, but when these situations must be faced they are associated with significant levels of distress.

✦ *The fear/anxiety is disproportionate relative to the situation and sociocultural norms.*

> This comes back to the need to differentiate between "normal" anxiety and the intensity of an anxiety disorder. Social anxiety disorder is not the same as shyness or mild nervousness. The distress experienced is significantly greater than what might be expected of an average person in that situation. The nature of the triggering

situation(s) and sociocultural norms should be considered in the context of the particular individual experiencing the symptoms rather than being interpreted based on the clinician's views and/or mainstream cultural norms.

✦ *The symptoms are persistent, usually lasting for at least 6 months.*

✦ *The symptoms cause "clinically significant distress or impairment in social, occupational, or other areas of functioning."*

Social anxiety disorder is linked to higher dropout rates from school, and an increased likelihood of being single/unmarried. It can lead to chronic social isolation, and overall quality of life can be significantly affected.

✦ *The symptoms are not due to the direct effect of a drug or medical condition, and are not better accounted for by another mental disorder.*

Someone may have more than one anxiety disorder diagnosis, but multiple diagnoses should not be given in cases where a single diagnosis can best account for all of the symptoms that are present.

✦ *If an outwardly visible medical condition is present, the symptoms are clearly unrelated or out of proportion to what might be expected.*

For example, if someone has had skin grafts because of a major burn, the social anxiety would be either unrelated or excessive compared to what would be expected of an average person with skin grafts. This isn't necessarily clear-cut, but it may be useful to consider whether all of the feared situations and potential consequences relate to the visible condition. If someone with a skin graft on their leg worries about being humiliated by spilling a drink, that's likely unrelated.

There is a performance-only subtype of social anxiety disorder that specifically involves impairment in professional roles that are associated with some type of performance in front of others, such as public speaking. The anxiety associated with this particular subtype doesn't spill over to affect other types of social interactions.

People with social anxiety disorder may lack assertiveness. They may speak softly, limit eye contact, and blush often. Self-medicating with substances like alcohol is common.

While social anxiety disorder is sometimes confused with shyness (a personality trait), they are not the same thing, and only about 12% of people who describe themselves as shy also have social anxiety disorder. Introversion is another personality trait that is sometimes confused with social anxiety. For introverts, social situations require a significant expenditure of mental energy, and they need time alone to recharge. A person with social anxiety disorder may be naturally extroverted and have a desire to socialize, but because of their illness they're unable to engage with others the way they would like to.

The usual age of onset for social anxiety disorder is between 8 and 15 years old. The onset may be gradual, or it may be more sudden and prompted by a specific negative event. Social anxiety disorder seldom emerges for the first time in adulthood, and when it does it's typically triggered by highly stressful or humiliating life events. The disorder is more common in females than males, and rates appear to be higher in the United States than elsewhere in the world.

※ ※ ※

Autumn Skies Blog's Story (Social Anxiety Disorder)

When I was in preschool, my mom had a term for it – Parallel Playing. We've talked about my first year of pre-k over the years. I didn't often interact directly with the other kids, but I could tell you what everyone did that day. I played, but didn't interact. I think that was one of the first signs. Social anxiety was not "a thing" then. It was being shy.

Over the years, I more or less conformed to "social norms" in terms of directly interacting with my peers. I was never comfortable doing so, as I was always worried about being judged, my peers secretly not liking me, or making an idiot of myself. The list is long. However, I found ways to manage.

Adult life is a bit more "complex." There aren't quite as many social rules and guidelines in daily life. In work-life, I have a method. I watch how others interact, watch their mannerisms, their sense of humour, how they communicate. After watching others for a while, I then base how much "me" I let through dependent on how others act, never letting out more than anyone else. Sometimes, this gets difficult, especially as I work with smaller groups directly, and there is less room for my "method." I find the most generic parts of myself to share. New places and people are the hardest.

Mental illness is not always the most accepted, especially in a work or more public environment. The problem is, social anxiety is at its finest in those situations. The majority of my free time, I am home, by myself, watching Netflix. I communicate primarily via text, as calling anyone sets off loud alarms in my head. Since my full time job involves socializing, I choose to spend my free time minimally socializing.

Mentally, it is a constant complex web of emotions. Wanting to be around people and wanting to be liked, but constantly living in fear after almost every word you said that this would be the moment they figure out you aren't special and that it's time to move on to the next person.

Physically, for me, it comes out in playing with my hair, biting my nails or cuticles, chewing gum, keeping a beverage nearby to sip on, fidgeting, slightly "rocking/swaying" (it's been likened to a "mother's rock"), and a lot of biting my lips and inside of my cheeks. Just in hopes of relieving some of the anxiety, or at least distracting myself enough to get through a social event.

– *Autumn Skies Blog*

❋ ❋ ❋

Panic Disorder

Panic attacks have highly physical symptoms, which can feel like a medical emergency. The symptoms numbered 1-13 below constitute a panic attack, which may occur in the context of multiple disorders other than panic disorder. The remaining criteria are required to be given a specific diagnosis of panic disorder.

Not everyone who has panic attacks is diagnosed with panic disorder. Someone who experiences panic attacks as part of generalized anxiety disorder might be given a diagnosis of generalized anxiety disorder with panic attacks. An additional diagnosis of panic disorder would only be given if it better explained the panic attacks.

The diagnosis of panic disorder involves the following criteria:

✦ *There are recurrent panic attacks that are unexpected and involve a sudden surge of intense fear, with 4 or more of the following symptoms:*

> These symptoms appear out of nowhere and generally hit their peak within a few minutes. Many of the symptoms result from activation of the sympathetic nervous system's fight or flight response, and they are very physical in nature. Hyperventilation leads to a drop in levels of carbon dioxide in the blood, which then fuels a number of the other symptoms.

To be diagnosed with panic disorder, at least some of the panic attacks must have no identifiable trigger.

1. *Increased heart rate or a feeling of the heart pounding*

2. *Sweating*

3. *Shakiness*

4. *Feeling like it's difficult to breathe*

5. *Feelings of choking*

6. *Chest pain*

    The person may feel as though they're having a heart attack.

7. *Abdominal discomfort or nausea*

8. *Dizziness*

    The person may feel unsteady or as though they are about to faint.

9. *Feeling hot or cold*

10. *Numbness/tingling*

11. *Derealization or depersonalization*

    These are forms of dissociation, and are explained in detail in the chapter on dissociative disorders.

12. *Fear of losing control*

13. *Feeling of impending death*

✦ *An attack is followed by at least a month of either/both of:*

  • *Persistent worry about having more panic attacks and being subject to the harm that may result from them*

    Often there is concern about physical health repercussions, like having a heart attack or a seizure. There may also be worry about the potential social consequences resulting from being observed by others while having a panic attack.

  • *Avoidance behaviours in an attempt to prevent panic attacks*

    These avoidance behaviours may involve major changes in daily routines in order to avoid circumstances that are thought to trigger an attack. However, since diagnosis of this disorder requires the presence of unexpected panic attacks, these avoidance behaviours are unlikely to have a significant impact on the actual frequency of panic attacks.

 The symptoms are not the direct result of a drug or medical condition, and are not better accounted for by another mental disorder.

If the panic attacks only occur in the context of social anxiety disorder, a specific phobia, OCD, or PTSD, then that disorder might better account for the symptoms than an additional diagnosis of panic disorder.

❖

The frequency of panic attacks is highly variable. Once a week is considered moderate frequency, but some people may go years between attacks. Some, but not necessarily all, of the attacks will meet the full symptom threshold for a panic attack, while others may have fewer symptoms.

While the diagnosis requires the presence of unexpected panic attacks, about half of people with panic disorder will also have panic attacks that do have an identifiable trigger. Some unexpected panic attacks can be nocturnal, with an individual being awoken from sleep in a state of panic. These occur in around 1/4 to 1/3 of people diagnosed with panic disorder.

Prevalence rates vary amongst different countries and cultural groups, which may be related to different attributions for the symptoms. The disorder is twice as common in females as in males. The onset of panic disorder may begin in the teens, and peaks in the early 20s. Rates are lower in older adults, which may be the result of symptoms naturally starting to ease off with older age.

There appears to be some linkage between childhood sexual and/or physical abuse and panic disorder. Smoking is a risk factor, as is a neurotic temperament. Often there are some sort of identifiable stressors in the months leading up to the initial panic attack. A history of panic attacks within the last 12 months is associated with an increased risk of suicide. It's common to have another mental illness diagnosis that is co-occurring, such as another anxiety disorder or a mood disorder.

Johnzelle's Story (Panic Disorder)

To me, diagnosis is simply a starting point for a discussion about mental health. Diagnosis is NOT a label, a prognosis, or an excuse. The purpose of diagnosis is to increase awareness of one's symptoms and experiences… and it's often required for providers to bill your insurance for mental health services. The experience of getting diagnosed has been an ongoing process for me. Over the years, my diagnosis has changed depending on my provider. With that being said, I have been diagnosed with major depressive disorder, panic disorder, generalized anxiety disorder, and adjustment disorder. I know that I don't have all four of these conditions; however, providers often don't take the time to clarify diagnoses with their patients, especially when they've been in services elsewhere.

The DSM-5, which this book focuses on, is thought to be the ultimate mental health bible; however, I disagree with some of its components (and yeah, a licensed therapist just blasphemed the holy book of mental health!). When I was in grad school, I was taught that diagnosis was definite and fixed for the most part. In my experiences of both diagnosing clients and venturing through my own recovery process, I have become more irritated with the DSM-5's approach to fitting people neatly into a single box. I look at diagnosis as fluid and malleable.

I was diagnosed with panic disorder when I was in my junior year of undergrad. I was having upwards to ten panic attacks daily and was feeling pretty hopeless. I've noticed that after an extended period of anxiety that I tend to experience depressive symptoms (hence the misdiagnosis of major depressive disorder). This seems to be common for anxiety sufferers, as the hyperactive fight-flight-freeze response can drain you of your energy and motivation after a while.

Panic disorder differs from generalized anxiety disorder in that the panic attacks are more pronounced; however, those with GAD can also have panic attacks (the DSM-5 calls this a "specifier"). When I was in undergrad, the panic disorder was fitting, as I experienced the racing thoughts, sweating, lightheadedness, tearfulness, and abdominal discomfort of panic attacks. I also experienced derealization, which made me occasionally feel like I existed outside of myself. I also developed anxiety about having future panic attacks. I began to avoid situations that I feared would trigger a panic attack.

During that year, I sought the help of a therapist for the first time and began anxiety medication. Once I learned some coping skills and found a good medication regimen, the panic attacks reduced. As I moved and changed therapists, I was diagnosed with similar anxiety disorders based on the severity at that time; more specifically, adjustment disorder with anxiety and generalized anxiety disorder. Currently, I would say that my diagnosis is more of a generalized anxiety disorder with the panic attack specifier; however, it is well managed with medication and regular visits to a therapist. That's right, folks! Therapists go to therapy too!

My anxiety diagnosis impacted my recovery journey in a big way. After experiencing therapy in my junior year, I chose to go to graduate school to become a therapist. I am now a licensed professional counsellor in private practice using my experiences to help others along in their journeys. I like the saying, "You can't stop the waves, but you can learn how to surf." It concisely describes what it's like to live with anxiety and the journey towards managing it. I consider my mental illness to be a strength that has enabled me to understand and connect with others going through life's struggles.

– *Johnzelle Anderson, LPC, Panoramic Counseling*

❊ ❊ ❊

Generalized Anxiety Disorder (GAD)

Like the name implies, generalized anxiety disorder (GAD) is an anxiety disorder that is generalized across multiple different areas of a person's life, and the anxiety isn't limited to specific focal areas.

The diagnostic criteria for generalized anxiety disorder are:

✦ *There is excessive anxiety/worry that occurs on most days for a period of at least 6 months. This anxiety pertains to a number of different areas of the person's life.*

The level of anxiety/worry is disproportionate to the situation(s). The anxiety occurs across multiple contexts, which helps to establish it as a generalized disorder rather than a specific phobia.

✦ *The worry is difficult to control.*

Unlike "normal" worry, it is very difficult for an affected person to distract themselves, shift focus to other cognitive tasks, or talk themselves out of it.

✦ *The anxiety/worry involves at least 3 of the following that are present for the majority of the 6 month period:*

Note that these symptoms are different from a panic attack, and they are present chronically rather than occurring in episodic bursts.

- *Restlessness*

- *Easily tired*

- *Problems with concentration*

- *Irritability*

- *Muscle tension*

     The muscle tension may result in shakiness, twitching, and soreness.

- *Insomnia*

✦ *The symptoms "cause clinically significant distress or impairment in social, occupational, or other important areas of functioning."*

✦ *The symptoms are not due to the direct effects of a drug or medical condition, and are not better accounted for by another mental disorder.*

     Other conditions to rule out include other anxiety disorders or PTSD. Some medications can potentially cause anxiety symptoms.

The DSM-5 describes several features that help to differentiate an anxiety disorder from the "normal" anxiety that everyone experiences from time to time:

- The worry is excessive and has a significant impact on overall functioning.

- The worry is more intense, longer-lasting, more distressing, and often occurs without triggers.

- People with anxiety disorders typically experience physical symptoms.

Individuals with generalized anxiety disorder often experience other associated physical symptoms besides those listed in the diagnostic criteria, such as sweating, nausea, and diarrhea. Palpitations, difficulty breathing, and dizziness are less common than in panic disorder. Generalized anxiety disorder can be associated with stress-related physical conditions such as recurrent headaches or irritable bowel syndrome.

Generalized anxiety disorder appears to be more common amongst people of European descent and inhabitants of first world countries. In a given year just around 3% of adults in the United States will experience GAD. It is twice as common in females as in males.

The age of onset can vary considerably, although onset before the teens in rare. Earlier onset is associated with a greater level of impairment and greater risk of developing another mental disorder. There tends to be moderate to serious functional disability associated with GAD.

There may be some association between parental overprotectiveness and the development of GAD, although this hasn't been clearly established. A neurotic temperament, involving a natural tendency to experience more negative emotions as part of one's personality, is linked to an increased risk of developing GAD.

❄ ❄ ❄

Christina's Story (Generalized Anxiety Disorder)

All my life I suffered from anxiety. I was always anxious for anything. I was always anxious for doctors' appointments, dentist appointments, giving a presentation, or an exam at school. Also confrontation and people being angry at me make me anxious. I knew it was more than just being anxious. I can't function normally in my life because of it. The difference between anxiety and an anxiety disorder is that you can't live a normal life. Anxiety takes place in every aspect of your life, such as making it difficult to find a job, go to school, or do everyday life things such as getting out of bed in the morning.

I asked for help in the Netherlands but I felt that they didn't help me enough or didn't take me as seriously as in Spain. Two years ago I went to the doctors in Spain and got medications prescribed. It was then that I got the diagnosis of having generalized anxiety disorder. It felt good to finally know what was happening to me. I have always felt all those symptoms like being nauseous, dizzy, headaches, my heart beating fast, and feeling like you are going crazy and like you are going to die. I feel this and so much more. It was the first time in my life that I felt like I'm not actually going crazy. I accepted that I have a mental illness. Mental illnesses are real and there's nothing to be ashamed of.

There's still so much taboo of mental health illnesses. I wish with speaking up about it that it can end one day. There's also a lot of misinformation with it. Anxiety isn't just being anxious. It's much more than that. It's feeling like you are going crazy, it's avoiding your fears because you think you can't deal with them without having a panic attack, and it's constantly thinking the worst of a situation. People who don't know what it's like to live with anxiety just say to snap out of it or to think positive. If it would be that simple I and everyone who deals with it would have already done that. There's not a magic cure to it.

I think that a diagnosis can help a person to understand what they are going through. They would feel less alone when they see others are also struggling with the same illness. That's how I felt when I began blogging. The blogging community is so amazing, so open and so beautiful. I feel less alone hearing that other people are going through the same thing. Sharing our struggles makes us more compassionate towards ourselves and others. We can build beautiful relationships when we are open, vulnerable, and honest to each other. Nowadays, I think that maybe I have to ask for help again to be able to deal with anxiety better. I sometimes take a benzo to help me deal with it.

I hope with speaking up about my story more people will do it too. We have to know that we aren't alone in this. We are going through our own battles. The world needs more kindness, love, and compassion. In this sometimes fake world it's important that we are there for each other and that we help others in our struggles. We can guide each other home and make each other feel safe. Feel your feelings. Our feelings are valid. It's okay to not be okay. We are all in this together! Together we are standing strong!

– *Christina, Sea of Words*

Bipolar and Related Disorders

Bipolar disorder, which was known in the past as manic depressive disorder, is a type of mood disorder that involves episodes of mania and/or hypomania, and in most cases episodes of depression. It is sometimes abbreviated as BAD (bipolar affective disorder), not to be confused with BPD (borderline personality disorder).

This chapter covers bipolar disorder types I and II, as well as the related cyclothymic disorder. There are also diagnoses for bipolar disorder induced by a substance or medical condition, as well as an unspecified bipolar disorder diagnosis, but those won't be covered here.

Bipolar I is diagnosed when there has been a full manic episode. People with bipolar I are likely to also have depressive and/or hypomanic episodes over the course of the illness, but these are not required to make a diagnosis. The diagnosis of bipolar II requires at least one hypomanic episode, which is less severe than mania, and at least one depressive episode. Cyclothymic disorder is a related condition, but it is not a type of bipolar disorder. If someone meets the criteria for bipolar disorder, that automatically rules out cyclothymic disorder.

While sometimes bipolar I is described as being more severe than bipolar II, the depressive aspect of bipolar II can be devastating, and there's really no way to make broad characterizations about illness severity. However, by definition the manic episodes in bipolar I are more severe in terms of number and severity of symptoms compared to the hypomanic episodes of bipolar II.

While bipolar disorder often involves discrete episodes of mania/hypomania and episodes of depression, sometimes people will experience episodes with "mixed" features. These involve concurrent manic and depressive symptoms. Mood episodes with mixed features can be particularly challenging to treat. Some bipolar illness presentations may be characterized as rapid cycling depending on the frequency of the mood episodes. Rapid cycling involves at least four mood episodes (or two full mania-depression cycles) in a year. Sometimes the terms ultra rapid cycling and ultradian cycling may be used to describe more frequent mood cycles, but these terms do not appear in the DSM-5.

Sometimes there is some confusion about the difference between bipolar disorder and borderline personality disorder. Borderline personality disorder is actually more closely associated with rapid, frequent mood swings (also known as mood lability) than bipolar disorder is. Mood swings are not included as a diagnostic criterion for bipolar disorder. The diagnostic criteria for borderline personality disorder will be covered in the upcoming chapter on personality disorders, but the two illnesses are actually quite different, especially looking from a longitudinal perspective. Some people may have co-occurring bipolar disorder and borderline personality disorder, and early in the assessment process it can sometimes be difficult to figure out which disorder is the most responsible for particular symptoms.

※ ※ ※

Mood Episode Criteria

Before moving on to the specific bipolar diagnoses, we'll cover the diagnostic criteria for each type of mood episode (manic, hypomanic, and depressive). Mood episodes refers to distinct periods of symptoms, whereas the overarching diagnosis refers to the illness in its entirety.

Manic episode

The criteria for a manic episode are:

✦ *There is elevated or irritable mood combined with significantly elevated energy, lasting almost all day and almost every day for at least one week.*

> Someone who is manic may appear euphoric, as though they are on top of the world. Alternatively, they may be highly irritable. The increased energy may lead to the person undertaking multiple major, unrealistic projects in areas that they may know little about. There may be mood lability, with rapid, brief shifts in mood. If the person's symptoms are severe enough that they need to be admitted to hospital, the 1-week time frame is not required to make a diagnosis.

✦ *During that period, there are at least 3 of the following symptoms (or 4 if mood is irritated rather than elevated) that represent a significant change from the person's normal pattern:*

> It can be easy to look at the symptom criteria and think almost anyone could be diagnosed with mania. However, the symptoms must represent a significant deviation from "normal". This is not some vague societal generalization of what normal should be, but rather what is normal for that specific individual given their pattern of experience over time. Sometimes information from secondary sources like family

members is needed to determine what that person's "normal" is, while other times the symptoms are so severe that it's obvious very quickly that they represent a pathological process.

The number of symptoms required is higher if the person is experiencing irritated mood rather than elevated mood. This is because irritated mood is less specific to bipolar disorder than elevated mood is, and therefore a higher symptom threshold must be met to be certain that the presentation is in fact manic.

- *Elevated self-esteem or grandiosity*

    This grandiosity may be extreme to the point of being delusional. Specific delusional beliefs may vary, but a common theme is having special abilities, or connections to well known public figures. This differs from narcissism in that the grandiosity, or at least that high level of grandiosity, is not typical for the individual.

    Clinicians must be careful not to fall into the trap of making assumptions regarding the veracity of patients' expressed beliefs. A patient may in reality have a close connection to someone famous, and it may be helpful to talk to friends/family to clarify this. Even if the connection is in fact real, often a manic person who is experiencing grandiosity will place undue emphasis and importance on it, or may overestimate their own influence on the famous person or responsibility for their success.

- *Decreased need for sleep*

    This is quite different from the insomnia that occurs in depression, in which a person feels exhausted and would give anything to sleep, but they just can't. When manic, someone may go days without sleep and still not feel tired. Sleep may be considered a waste of valuable time that could better be spent doing something productive with their mental energy and following through on grandiose plans.

- *Talkative, with pressured speech*

    It's not uncommon for "normal" people to be talkative, but pressured speech is quite distinctive. It's as though the person is tripping over themselves trying to get the words out fast enough in order to keep up with the rush of ideas going through their mind. Want to get a word in edgewise? You might have to steamroll right over the person, because there may not be any natural break to get a word in; this is something I have to do as a nurse when conducting assessments in order to keep the interview on track.

There may also be dramatic flair associated with speech, such as singing or enthusiastic gesturing. When someone's mood is irritated, the talkativeness may turn into a loud tirade.

- *Thoughts racing*

  This can include rapid switches from one topic to another. If someone jumps from one topic to a somewhat related one and doesn't return to the original thought, this is referred to as tangentiality. The manic person may seem to have so many ideas that they just can't finish one before rushing on to the next.

- *Easily distracted*

  While impaired concentration in depression is often bothersome for people, distractibility in mania may not always be subjectively perceived as problematic. The distractions may even be viewed positively by people who are highly manic, as they become excited by new ideas. In less severe manic episodes when people are trying to maintain their usual daily activities, the distractibility may be more distressing.

- *Increased activity, which may be purposeless or directed towards accomplishing goals*

  People may become hyper-social, frequently contacting others they may normally have little to do with. They may also send repeated, sometimes lengthy messages to people they don't know, such as media outlets or major public figures. People who are normally creative may become hyper-productive with whatever their creative medium may be. Regardless of the particular activities, the person seems to keep going like the Energizer bunny.

- *Engaging in high-risk activities, such as excessive spending or irresponsible sexual behaviour*

  These are often activities that the manic person wouldn't even consider doing in such a manner when they're well. These behaviours may have serious lasting repercussions, and may be highly distressing for the individual once the mania has cleared. These manic behaviours may result in significant debt, or someone may contract a sexually transmitted infection or become pregnant from unprotected sex.

✦ *"The mood disturbance is sufficiently severe to cause marked impairment in social or occupational functioning or to necessitate hospitalization to prevent harm to self or others, or there are psychotic features."*

This helps to distinguish mania from "normal" as well as the less severe hypomania. If psychosis is present an episode is automatically considered manic rather than hypomanic.

✦ *The episode is not due to the direct effects of a drug or medical condition.*

Certain medications, such as steroids, may precipitate mania, but this would not count toward a diagnosis of bipolar I or II. Where this can get a bit more complicated is if the mania has emerged during antidepressant treatment for depression. To qualify for a diagnosis of bipolar I or II, the full criteria for mania/hypomania must continue to be met "beyond the physiological effect of the treatment" that precipitated the manic/hypomanic symptoms. However, stopping a medication does not immediately put an end to the physiological effect of that same treatment, so it may be impossible to pinpoint exactly when the drug stops having an influence. Possible medication-induced mania requires close monitoring in order to get a good understanding of timing and the clearest possible picture of what is causing what.

People who are manic may present themselves in a manner that is flamboyant or sexually provocative and is a considerable departure from their usual appearance. This may include revealing clothing or heavy makeup that's quite different from the individual's norm. Inferences about mania should never be based on someone's appearance without having a baseline for comparison. For example, if someone routinely wears heavy makeup and miniskirts there's no reason to consider that pathological. However, if a patient who is well known to a clinician shows up for an appointment with a major change in dress/makeup, and this is a pattern for them during their manic episodes, then that may be a warning sign of emerging mania.

Hypomanic episode

The symptoms of a hypomanic episode are similar to the symptoms of mania, but there are fewer symptoms and a lesser degree of severity required to meet the diagnostic criteria. If psychotic symptoms are present or the symptoms are severe enough to warrant inpatient hospitalization, the episode would be considered manic rather than hypomanic.

The criteria for a hypomanic episode are:

✦ *There is abnormally and persistently elevated (or irritable) mood and energy, most of the day and nearly every day for at least 4 days in a row.*

This criterion represents a lesser severity than mania, and there is also has a shorter duration of symptoms required for diagnosis (4 days rather than one week).

✦ *During this period, there are 3 or more of the following (or four if mood is only irritable), which are a noticeable change from the person's usual behaviour:*

The symptoms themselves are very similar to the symptoms of mania, but in hypomania there are fewer symptoms and they are less severe. The changes are noticeable rather than significant. This means that they are sufficient that they're often recognized by close friends and family, but they may not necessarily be overt enough to be noticed by others who don't know the person well.

As with mania, since irritability is less specific to hypomania than elevated mood, an additional symptom criterion must be met to ensure that hypomania is the appropriate diagnosis.

- *Elevated self-esteem or grandiosity*

    This might not be immediately recognizable as being pathological to someone who isn't acquainted with the affected person, but others close to the individual may notice a distinct change. Grandiosity in hypomania doesn't reach delusional proportions as it can in mania.

- *Decreased need for sleep*
- *More talkative than usual*

    In hypomania, a person's talkative speech pattern might be not quite as rapid as in mania, and may be easier to interrupt.

- *Racing thoughts*
- *Easily distracted*
- *Increased goal-oriented activity or psychomotor agitation*

    Compared to mania, the increased goal-oriented activity in hypomania is likely to be somewhat more purposeful, and may involve hyperactivity in areas the individual is already interested in or working on.

- *Excessive involvement in high-risk activities*

These activities may be impulsive and poorly thought through, but may not carry quite the same level of risk for negative consequences compared to mania.

✦ *There is an "unequivocal change in functioning" that is not typical of the individual when they are well, but there is not marked impairment or a need for hospitalization.*

This contrasts with the "marked impairment" that's required to diagnose a manic episode. An unequivocal change means that there is clearly a deviation from the individual's "normal", while marked impairment means that there is a large magnitude of deviation from normal. If the symptoms are severe enough to warrant hospitalization or if there are psychotic symptoms, then that would automatically be considered a manic episode.

✦ *The episode is not due to the direct effect of a drug or medical condition.*

Caution must be used in making a diagnosis when symptoms emerge during treatment for depression, as antidepressant-induced hypomanic symptoms are not enough on their own to warrant a bipolar I or II diagnosis. The same physical health medications that can potentially cause mania may also cause hypomania, so this needs to be ruled out as well.

Major depressive episode

A major depressive episode (MDE) refers to a single episode, and is not a stand-alone diagnosis, unlike the very similar sounding major depressive disorder. The potential symptoms of an MDE are the same whether they occur in the context of major depressive disorder or bipolar disorder, although the treatment can be quite different. Bipolar depressive episodes are not inherently any more or less severe than episodes in major depressive disorder, and there can be considerable variation in symptoms from one individual to the next.

The criteria for a major depressive episode in bipolar disorder are as follows, and are explained in detail in the chapter on depressive disorders.

✦ *The depressive symptoms must last for at least 2 weeks and be present almost all of the day, almost every day. One of the first two symptoms must be present, along with 4 other symptoms:*
  • *Depressed mood*

- *Significant loss of interest/pleasure in almost all activities*
- *Significant change in appetite and/or unintentional weight loss/gain.*
- *Disruption in sleep, which can be either insomnia or sleeping excessively*
- *Objectively observable changes in the speed of movements, either slowing (psychomotor retardation) or agitation.*
- *Decreased energy*
- *Feelings of worthlessness or guilt that are out of proportion to the situation*
- *Problems with concentration and decision-making*
- *Suicidal ideation*

✦ *The symptoms cause "clinically significant distress or impairment in social, occupational, or other important areas of functioning."*

✦ *The symptoms must not be due to the direct effects of either a drug or another health condition.*

❋ ❋ ❋

Bipolar I Disorder

Bipolar I is diagnosed when someone has met the criteria for a manic episode. Commonly hypomanic and depressive episodes will also occur over the course of the illness, but these aren't required for the diagnosis. The depressive episodes may have a greater effect on overall functioning than the manic or hypomanic episodes.

The criteria for bipolar I disorder are:

✦ *There has been at least one manic episode.*

At least one episode has met the full criteria for mania as described above. A hypomanic or depressive episode may occur before or after the manic episode.

✦ *The mood episode(s) are not better accounted for by another mental illness.*

33

Schizoaffective disorder, which will be covered in the chapter on psychotic disorders, is one of the disorders that should be ruled out. It involves mood episodes and psychosis, and someone would only be diagnosed with the illness that best accounted for the pattern of symptoms that is experienced.

Bipolar disorder is chronic in nature, and the pattern of episodes may evolve over time. The illness often begins with mood episodes interspersed with periods of remission, but some people do not achieve full remission between episodes, especially later on in the course of their illness.

The average age of onset is 18 years old, but it can also develop later in life. Bipolar I occurs with equal frequency in males and females, but males tend to have more manic episodes and females tend to have more depressive episodes, mixed episodes, and rapid cycling. Rates are twice as high in high-income countries compared to low-income countries (1.4% vs 0.7% yearly prevalence). The suicide rate for people with bipolar I is between 10-15%.

The diagnostic specifiers for bipolar mood episodes are almost identical to those for major depressive disorder. The same specifiers can be applied to both bipolar I and II. They describe how the illness is presenting at a specific point in time, and may fluctuate over the course of the illness. They do not change the underlying diagnosis of bipolar disorder; they just give further detail about a given episode. The specifiers are:

- **with anxious distress**: This specifier is used when symptoms of anxiety occur specifically in the context of a mood episode.

- **with mixed features**: This specifier is used when a person meets the diagnostic criteria for one pole (mania or depression) but also has 3 or more non-overlapping symptoms from the opposite pole. An episode would be described as either manic or depressive with mixed features depending on the pole in which more symptoms were present.

- **rapid cycling**: Four or more mood episodes occurring within the space of a year is considered to be rapid cycling. The terms ultra rapid cycling and ultradian cycling are sometimes used to refer to more frequent cycling between mania and depression, but they're not used in the DSM-5.

- **with melancholic features**: This involves depressive episodes with prominent psychomotor retardation and excessive guilt.

- **atypical features**: Atypical depressive episodes include increased sleep and appetite.

- **psychotic features (mood congruent or incongruent)**: Psychotic symptoms may occur during manic or depressive episodes. Mood congruent psychotic symptoms are consistent with the individual's mood state, such as grandiose delusions during a manic episode or delusional guilt in a depressive episode. Psychotic symptoms may also be mood incongruent, meaning they're unrelated to the prominent mood-related themes.

- **with catatonia**: Catatonic features involve significant changes in movements and reactivity to the environment, and are described in detail in the chapter on psychosis.

- **with peripartum onset**: While peripartum/postpartum depression may be more widely recognized, mania and hypomania may also emerge around the same time.

- **with seasonal pattern**: The seasonal pattern may affect periods of mania/hypomania, depression, or both.

❄ ❄ ❄

Katie's Story (Bipolar I)

In my episodes of manic psychosis, I experienced a wide variety of psychotic symptoms. I couldn't tell the difference between reality and the things that seemed to be there but really weren't. Sound scary? It was. Here are four basic types of symptoms I had while in manic psychosis.

Delusions: While I have a strong faith in the God of the Bible, I was particularly prone to developing a type of delusion, especially in my bipolar manic psychotic state, that related to God or something in the Bible. At these times, I was overcome with the sense that I was a person from the scriptures, or that I encountered angels and demons in human form. This is also known as hyper-religiosity – being preoccupied with religious symbolism and meanings – and is a symptom of bipolar disorder.

Paranoia: This extreme type of fear plagued my mind and induced anxiety and anxiety attacks at times. I wrestled with the fear of the FBI bugging our house (another delusion), the fear that Tom Cruise was trying to persecute me (delusion of course), and the fear that I was being watched in the spiritual realm and a target of spiritual attack. My number one fear that I could articulate in this state of mind at one point was the Illuminati. Obviously, reason, good sense, and logic evaded me and I let paranoia get the best of me at times.

Hallucinations: My brain made up auditory and visible things that were not really there, like when I thought I saw Tom Cruise standing on the street corner as I passed by in a trolley. I thought I saw a man physically transported through thin air. I heard demonic voices in my head chanting loudly (they lasted momentarily). I saw the face of an ex-boyfriend in my husband's face, and saw my first boyfriend bicycling past me twice in a few minutes, in the same direction. These are examples of the weird ways my mind played tricks on me in manic psychosis.

Visions: I want to distinguish that I hallucinated but also had visions. The visions were different from hallucinations in that they were like watching a dream but while I was half-asleep, or like a daydream that was so vivid you could see it through your eyes into your mind's eye. I had visions of being in Heaven, a crowd of angels surrounding me and cheering, symbolic visions of books flying through the air like birds, and a woman dying in childbirth. They happened at different times in the few months I was off my bipolar medications. After I returned to my medications, they stopped.

– *Katie Dale, Bipolar Brave*

❄ ❄ ❄

Bipolar II Disorder

To be diagnosed with bipolar II, there must be at least one hypomanic episode and at least one depressive episode. If there was a manic episode at any point, bipolar II would not be applicable; the diagnosis would shift to bipolar I. If psychotic symptoms are present during an episode, that episode would be considered manic rather than hypomanic and therefore would be diagnosed as bipolar I.

Major depressive episodes in bipolar II tend to occur more often and last longer compared to those in bipolar I. Unlike bipolar I, depression is required to meet the criteria for bipolar II.

If the first episode(s) of illness are depressive, someone may initially be diagnosed with major depressive disorder and then have the diagnosed changed to bipolar II once there's been a hypomanic episode, or if a more thorough history-taking uncovers previous hypomanic episodes.

The criteria for bipolar II are:

✦ *There must be at least 1 hypomanic episode.*

> The criteria for diagnosing a hypomanic episode are the same as those already listed. In bipolar II, 60-70% of hypomanic episodes occur immediately before or after a depressive episode.

✦ *There must be at least 1 major depressive episode.*

> The criteria for diagnosing a depressive episode are the same as those used in bipolar I and major depressive disorder.

✦ *"The symptoms of depression or the unpredictability caused by frequent alternation between periods of depression and hypomania cause clinically significant distress or impairment in social, occupational, or other important areas of functioning."*

> Even if individual hypomanic episodes don't have a major impact on functioning, the unpredictable switching between depression and hypomania can result in a greater negative impact on functioning than might otherwise be expected from the hypomanic episodes themselves.

Often people with bipolar II will initially seek out mental health care for a depressive episode. They may not see their hypomanic episodes as problematic, and may even view them in a positive light, so this is where getting information from family members may be helpful in making the correct diagnosis. People who associate increased creativity with their hypomania may be more reluctant to accept treatment, fearing the loss of this creative energy.

The yearly prevalence of bipolar II is 0.8% in the United States, and 0.3% internationally. The average age of onset is in the mid-20s. There is no clear difference in rates between males and females. In females, childbirth can be a trigger for the onset of hypomania.

People with bipolar II tend to have a greater number of lifetime mood episodes compared to either bipolar I disorder or major depressive disorder. Rapid cycling (4 or more mood episodes per year) occurs in 5-15% of people with bipolar II, and is associated with a worse prognosis. Around 1/3 of people with bipolar II have a suicide attempt at some point in their life.

Phyllis's Story (Bipolar II)

Each person has their own story about what it is like to live with a mental illness. Even two people with the same diagnosis can have vast differences in their experiences. This is my story and my experience living with bipolar II.

The mood swings are very difficult to deal with. They often leave me feeling like I am going crazy. One moment I am fine, then at the drop of a hat, I am depressed or hypomanic or even both! I think the thing that is most difficult for me to live with is the horrible depths of depression that I go through. Suicidal thinking can be a daily occurrence when I am in a depressive episode. I have never attempted suicide nor have I been hospitalized; I consider myself one of the lucky few. Sometimes I feel so tired that I can't even stand to breathe. So depressed that all I want to do is end the pain. I don't really want to die. Feeling alone and empty in a room full of loved ones is the worst. I know in my right mind that these people love me and would do anything to help me if I would only ask. But the depression tells me different. The depression tells me that I am a pitiful excuse for a human being. No one loves me or likes me. Everyone just acts like they do so they don't hurt my feelings. This feeling can go on for weeks. It gets to the point where it physically hurts.

Then, I wake up one morning and I am ready to get my life together! I have an immense amount of energy and the colours in the world are so intense! Everything sounds louder and more melodic. I want to do everything that is fun, whatever that is. I have learned how to deal with the hypomania. I have done many stupid, stupid things while hypomanic. Some even dangerous. But in the moment I didn't care, I was high without taking drugs. I was feeling exceptional and happy and that is all that mattered in that moment.

Then I crash. Hard. Back to the depressive thoughts. Back to the wanting to die. Back to thinking I'm not worthy. I want to hide away from the world and stay in the dark. It is then where I feel the chasm open. I am falling and the only thing to hold onto are slippery stalactites that line the chasm. It is swallowing me whole and welcoming me below are the vast amounts of stalagmites with their various pointed heights. I haven't hit the bottom yet.

Then, just as soon as it all started, you are back to feeling level. You look back and realize that you have just been on a roller coaster ride. And you know it will happen again. But you have to live in the here and now and not worry about what is going to come. Even though you keep watching for signs and you never really get comfortable in the stability. I feel horrible for my actions and putting everyone else though what I have gone through. These moods leave me feeling irritated, annoyed, and sometimes full of rage for no reason at all.

I have just explained to you what a typical month is for me. Medication doesn't make the episodes or feelings go away. They just lessen the severity. Medication is not magic, it is just a helpful tool. The disorder/disease is still ever-present.

– *Phyllis Engle, Color Me Bipolar*

✳ ✳ ✳

Cyclothymic Disorder

Cyclothymic disorder, sometimes referred to as cyclothymia, involves highs and lows that don't meet the full diagnostic criteria for either hypomania or depression. It's sometimes colloquially referred to as "bipolar lite", but this isn't really accurate, as cyclothymic disorder is a distinct diagnosis from bipolar disorder. While the disorders are related, cyclothymic disorder is not a type of bipolar disorder.

Many of the diagrams floating around on the internet showing mood levels in cyclothymic disorder don't get this quite right, and mistakenly depict cyclothymia as reaching the level of hypomania. The presence of a manic, hypomanic, or depressive episode at any point in time automatically rules out cyclothymic disorder.

While the symptoms themselves don't reach the level of hypomania or depression, what's particularly noteworthy with this illness is the chronicity of it. The illness is present for a significant amount of time, with only short symptom-free periods.

The criteria for cyclothymia are:

+ *For at least 2 years there have been multiple periods of hypomanic symptoms and periods of depressive symptoms without meeting the full diagnostic criteria for either.*

    While there are symptoms of both hypomania and depression, there is never a sufficient number or severity of symptoms to meet the criteria for a hypomanic or depressive episode. Therefore, it would be inaccurate to say someone with cyclothymia has multiple episodes of hypomania and depression; rather, they have periods of hypomanic and depressive symptoms.

+ *Over that 2-year span, these periods of symptoms have been present for at least half the time, with no break between symptoms lasting for more than 2 months.*

    Like the equivalent criterion for persistent depressive disorder (dysthymia), this establishes that the condition is chronic rather than episodic.

+ *The diagnostic criteria have not been met at any point in time for a depressive, manic, or hypomanic episode.*

If these mood episodes are present, then major depressive disorder or bipolar disorder would be the more appropriate diagnosis.

✦ *The symptoms are not better explained by another mental illness or the direct effects of a drug or medical condition.*

✦ "The symptoms cause clinically significant distress or impairment in social, occupational, or other important areas of functioning."

The individual may function well during the periods where hypomanic symptoms are present, but in terms of the overall course of the disorder there is significant impairment in functioning, which is often related to cycles of unpredictable mood changes. As a result of this pattern, the person may be viewed by others as being temperamental, moody, or unpredictable.

The lifetime prevalence of cyclothymia is 1% or less, with no apparent differences between males and females. It tends to begin during the teens or early adult years. Between 15-50% of people with cyclothymic disorder will later progress to a diagnosis of bipolar disorder.

Depressive Disorders

Depressive disorders, like bipolar and related disorders, are a type of mood disorder. While mood is a key feature, there are multiple other accompanying symptoms, so these disorders are not just about mood. The different types of depression diagnoses include major depressive disorder, persistent depressive disorder (dysthymia), and premenstrual dysphoric disorder (which won't be covered in this chapter).

There are a variety of terms that are sometimes used to describe mood disorders other than the current diagnostic labels in the DSM-5. Some of these terms come from previous editions of the DSM, while others are layman's terms.

Terms that you might see or hear that aren't in the DSM-5 include:

- *clinical depression*: this generally refers to the DSM-5 diagnosis of major depressive disorder
- *endogenous depression:* this refers to a depression that is biological in nature rather than being situationally triggered
- *situational depression*: as opposed to endogenous depression, situational depression occurs as a result of difficult circumstances; this is loosely equivalent to adjustment disorder, which will be covered in the chapter on trauma and stressor-related disorders
- *unipolar depression*: this is equivalent to major depressive disorder, and is sometimes used to differentiate from bipolar depression

While the diagnostic terms currently in use are standardized in the current versions of the DSM and ICD, other terms that may be used are not standardized and therefore can mean different things depending on who's using them. Using proper terminology can help to avoid ambiguity in meaning.

❆ ❆ ❆

Major Depressive Disorder (MDD)

If you're reading this book most likely you're already aware that depression is not just about sadness. In fact, a diagnosis of major depressive disorder (MDD) can be made without an individual experiencing sadness at all. While it's a mood disorder, the symptoms of MDD encompass much more than just mood.

Major depressive disorder is a condition involving one or more major depressive episodes. The symptom patterns may vary from episode to episode and from individual to individual. There may be periods between episodes during which there is either partial or full remission of symptoms. As the course of illness progresses, those periods of remission may become fewer and further between, or even disappear altogether.

Major depressive episodes (MDEs) can occur in illnesses other than major depressive disorder. People with bipolar disorder and schizoaffective disorder can experience major depressive episodes, but they would not be given an additional diagnosis of major depressive disorder. Sometimes people will talk about having diagnoses of bipolar and depression, but in fact if someone has a diagnosis of bipolar disorder then major depressive disorder would not be an applicable diagnosis.

The diagnostic criteria for major depressive disorder are:

✦ *The symptoms must last for at least 2 weeks and be present almost all of the day, almost every day. One of the first two symptoms (i.e. depressed mood or loss of interest) must be present, along with 4 or more other symptoms:*

> The presence of symptoms almost all day, almost every day is a key element in distinguishing between illness and "normal" experience. The two week time frame is not intended to give any indication of how long a typical depressive episode lasts; rather, it's a minimum to help differentiate an illness episode from more transient mood changes.

• *Depressed mood*

> While some people with depression report feeling sad, sadness is not a requirement for the diagnosis. Depressed mood may cause feelings of hopelessness or numbness, or frequent tearfulness. Some people will experience irritability, and this is particularly common in children and adolescents.

• *Significant loss of interest/pleasure in almost all activities*

> The term "anhedonia" is used to describe an inability to feel pleasure. This loss of interest and pleasure extends to almost everything, including activities that are normally enjoyable for the individual. This may lead to social withdrawal and a loss of sex drive. Apathy, especially in combination with decreased energy, can result in less attention paid to hygiene compared to what is "normal" for the individual.

- *Significant change in appetite and/or unintentional weight loss/gain*

  Decreased appetite occurs more commonly than increased. The resulting change in weight can be significant. Weight changes due to deliberate diet/exercise do not count toward meeting this criterion, nor would weight gain resulting from starting a new medication. Increased appetite and weight gain may be seen in people who have depression with "atypical features".

- *Disruption in sleep, involving either insomnia or sleeping excessively*

  Most often people with depression will experience insomnia. This can involve difficulty falling asleep (initial insomnia), waking up during the night (middle insomnia), and/or waking up early in the morning (terminal insomnia). People with atypical depression, on the other hand, tend to sleep too much but don't feel rested.

- *Objectively observable changes in the speed of movements, either slowing ("psychomotor retardation") or agitation*

  This symptom is less common than others, and is more likely to be seen in more severe episodes and with "melancholic features". Psychomotor retardation involves the slowing of both movements and thought. Speech is often slower and of lower volume than normal, and there may be delayed responses to questions. Slowed movements are objectively observable, and may be quite apparent even to untrained observers. Psychomotor retardation isn't perceived the same way as decreased energy; rather, there may be a subjective sense of moving through molasses. Psychomotor agitation may take the form of restlessness, hand wringing, and/or tugging at clothes or other objects.

- *Decreased energy*

  This is one of the most common symptoms of depression, and it can have a significant impact on daily functioning. Decreased energy can impair one's ability to complete usual tasks, and may become severe enough that it is difficult to even get out of bed.

- *Feelings of worthlessness or guilt that are out of proportion to the situation*

  This may include unrealistic evaluations of the self and excessive rumination over past problems. There may be a disproportionate sense of responsibility for negative events occurring in the external environment, even if this is illogical. In some cases the guilt will become so firmly held it is considered delusional. This may be described as "guilt of delusional proportions."

- *Problems with concentration and decision-making*

  The cognitive effects of depression can include difficulties with memory, particularly in the elderly. There may be a decreased ability to handle multiple pieces of information, and decision-making may become overwhelming. More severe cognitive symptoms are associated with greater overall functional impairment and decreased responsiveness to antidepressants.

- *Suicidal ideation (suicidal thinking)*

  This may be passive (i.e. wishing one was dead) and/or active (i.e. having thoughts of taking one's own life). Thoughts of suicide may fluctuate in intensity, or they may be relatively consistent throughout a substantial part of the episode.

✦ *The symptoms cause "clinically significant distress or impairment in social, occupational, or other important areas of functioning."*

  For people with milder episodes, overall functioning may be maintained, but significantly more effort than usual is required. The level of functional impairment may be influenced by the specific combination of symptoms a person is experiencing, and may vary over the course of an episode.

✦ *The symptoms must not be due to the direct effects of either a drug or another health condition, and are not better accounted for by another mental disorder.*

  If someone has a history of mania or hypomania, bipolar disorder would likely be the most appropriate diagnosis. A person would not be diagnosed with both major depressive disorder and bipolar disorder at the same time, because the diagnosis of bipolar better accounts for the depressive symptoms than a diagnosis of MDD.

  If someone with an initial diagnosis of major depressive episode was later diagnosed with bipolar disorder because of a manic/hypomanic episode, the major depressive disorder diagnosis would no longer be valid. Around 5-10% of people diagnosed with major depressive disorder will later have that diagnosis changed to bipolar disorder.

  As mentioned earlier, some medications can cause symptoms of depression, and this needs to be ruled out. Similarly, certain medical conditions may cause depressive symptoms.

The DSM-5 explains that caution should be used when considering a depression diagnosis for someone who is experiencing bereavement, since some experiences similar to depression symptoms are to be expected with "normal" bereavement or other significant losses. However, it's also possible that bereavement can trigger the onset of a depressive episode, particularly in someone with a history of depression.

This is a change from the DSM-IV, which had a bereavement exclusion criterion, meaning someone could not be diagnosed as having a major depressive episode if they had recently experienced bereavement. While concerns have been raised that this change in the DSM-5 pathologizes normal human experience, according to the explanation given in the DSM-5 this was not the intention. The exact wording of this explanation, which is included alongside the diagnostic criteria, is:

> *"Responses to a significant loss (e.g., bereavement...) may include the feelings of intense sadness, rumination about the loss, insomnia, poor appetite, and weight loss noted in Criterion A, which may resemble a depressive episode. Although such symptoms may be understandable or considered appropriate to the loss, the presence of a major depressive episode in addition to the normal response to a significant loss should also be carefully considered. This decision inevitably requires the exercise of clinical judgment based on the individual's history and the cultural norms for the expression of distress in the context of loss."*

There are several specifier labels that can be added to a depression diagnosis to give more information about the characteristics of a particular depressive episode. These don't constitute distinct diagnoses, but rather serve as descriptors that may be added to the primary depression diagnosis to give further detail. For a given individual, symptom patterns may vary from episode to episode, and thus different specifiers may be applied at different points in time. The underlying diagnosis remains major depressive disorder throughout.

The specifier terms, which are very similar to those for bipolar disorder, are:

• **with anxious features**: This involves symptoms of anxiety that occur within the context of a depressive episode. If the anxiety symptoms are not clearly linked to mood episodes, a separate anxiety disorder diagnosis might be more appropriate.

• **with mixed features**: Three or more symptoms of mania/hypomania occur along with symptoms that fulfill the criteria for diagnosis of a major depressive episode. If at any point the full diagnostic criteria were met for mania/hypomania, a diagnosis of major depressive disorder would no longer be appropriate, and would be changed to bipolar disorder. Mixed depressive episodes are more common in bipolar depression, but may also occur in major depressive disorder.

- **with melancholic features:** This pattern of symptoms includes anhedonia, psychomotor retardation, and significant guilt. Symptoms tend to be worse in the morning. This subtype of depression appears to have a stronger biological element, and is less likely to be associated with situational triggers.

- **with atypical features:** This includes over-eating and over-sleeping, and may include a feeling of "leaden paralysis", as though the limbs are heavily weighed down. Often there is a longstanding pattern of sensitivity to interpersonal rejection.

- **with psychotic features:** The psychotic symptoms are often, but not always, congruent with mood. Delusional guilt is a common manifestation of psychosis in people with depression. Hallucinations may also occur. The different types of psychotic symptoms are discussed further in the chapter on psychotic disorders.

- **with catatonia:** Catatonia involves significant changes in motor behaviour and reactivity to the environment, and is like an extreme version of psychomotor retardation/agitation. More detail about catatonia is provided in the chapter on psychotic disorders.

- **with peripartum onset:** This is often referred to as postpartum depression. The term peripartum means around the time of birth. The DSM-5 does not consider postpartum depression to be a distinct diagnosis from major depressive disorder.

- **with seasonal pattern:** Often referred to as seasonal affective disorder, this involves depressive symptoms that occur at certain time of the year, typically in winter. Seasonal affective disorder is not a separate diagnosis from major depressive disorder in the DSM-5.

Major depressive episodes can also be specified as mild, moderate, or severe depending on how many symptoms are present. An episode would be considered severe if psychotic features were present. A major depressive episode (mild) still meets the diagnostic criteria for a major depressive episode, and is not the same as the "mild depression" that is sometimes colloquially referred to when describing dysthymia.

After a single episode of depression, there is a 60% chance of recurrence. After two episodes, that figure rises to 70%, and after three episodes there is a 90% risk of recurrence. The prognosis is worse when full remission of symptoms isn't attained between depressive episodes.

While not specifically listed as a symptom, it's not uncommon for people with depression to experience various physical issues, including pain and gastrointestinal problems.

There are no lab or imaging tests that can diagnose depression. However, there are certain changes in brain activity that have been observed in some people with depression, including hyperactivity in the system that controls the stress hormone cortisol and changes observable on MRI in the emotion regulation and reward seeking pathways in the brain.

❋ ❋ ❋

Ashley's Story (Major Depressive Disorder)

What has really stood out for me is how small a role the mood piece of my mood disorder can play in the overall scheme of things. My pattern of symptoms has varied over time, and often it's been symptoms other than mood that have done the most damage. Anhedonia is not necessarily all that distressing at any given moment, but when it's persistent and pervasive it truly sucks all the light out of the world, and that makes it hard to maintain hope.

Sometimes when things are quite bad I'll experience significant psychomotor retardation. It's like I'm trying to move but the world is resisting me. A lion could be trying to bite my butt and I wouldn't be able to move any faster. It can be pretty debilitating, because it becomes very hard for me to move around. Leaving the house can be almost impossible, and when I do it feels uncomfortable because I know the slowness is overtly apparent to others. It's a symptom that I've always been very aware of, but never had any power to control.

Cognitive symptoms have been a big problem with my depression. I get stupid – not in a self-critical sense, but literally. I'll be completely perplexed by simple choices like what brand of yogurt to get at the grocery store. There have been numerous times I've left stores empty-handed because I just don't seem to have the capacity to make any decisions. I've come up with various tricks to help compensate as best I can and avoid that feeling of overwhelmedness when there's not actually enough going on to be overwhelmed about.

Suicidal ideation has made multiple appearances over the course of my illness, and I've had multiple suicide attempts. For me it's been strongly linked with hopelessness, and a sense that there's nothing worth living for and the agony will never end. I haven't been impulsive with my suicidality. It's all been very (il)logically thought out. Sometimes people will say suicide is a selfish act. Thoughts of the effect on my family were what kept me hanging on as long as I did, until it got to the point where I just couldn't bear staying alive only for the sake of other people any longer. Had it not been for that commitment to my family and my pets, those suicide attempts would have happened much sooner, and there likely would have been more of them.

I'm not someone who has always been depressed, nor did I have a difficult upbringing or early life traumas. Depression swooped in when I was in my late 20s. While over the first few years I had periods of sustained remission lasting several years, the illness has since taken over my life more completely than I ever would have imagined. It's become treatment resistant, which has been hard to wrap my head around. I'm not my illness, but at the same time it's something that is always with me.

– Ashley Peterson, Mental Health @ Home

❉ ❉ ❉

Persistent Depressive Disorder (Dysthymia)

Persistent depressive disorder, also known by its former name dysthymia, is essentially a chronic, low-grade form of depression. While the symptoms are not as severe as those in major depressive disorder, the chronicity of the illness can have a major impact on overall quality of life. Colloquially, the term "mild depression" may sometimes be used to refer to persistent depressive disorder, but this is misleading since major depressive disorder and persistent depressive disorder are distinct diagnoses.

The diagnostic criteria for persistent depressive disorder are:

✦ *Depressed mood must be present for most of the day on most days for a period of at least 2 years.*

> This is different from major depressive disorder, which involves depressed mood almost *all day* almost *every day* over a shorter period of time. The minimum length of time the symptoms are present is much longer than major depressive disorder, in which the minimum time frame is 2 weeks.

✦ *There are 2 or more of the following symptoms:*

> Many of these correspond to symptoms of major depressive disorder. However, some of the more severe symptoms of MDD, like psychomotor retardation and suicidal ideation, are not included in the criteria for this diagnosis.

• *Changes in appetite*

> This replaces the significant change in weight/appetite criterion in MDD.

• *Change in sleep (insomnia or hypersomnia)*

• *Decreased energy*

• *Low self-esteem*

> This appears rather than the worthlessness/guilt criterion in MDD.

- *Problems with concentration and decision-making*
- *Feeling hopeless*

✦ *Over the 2-year period, symptoms have never been absent for more than 2 months at a time.*

This criterion helps to establish that this is a chronic, persistent condition rather than an episodic illness that's present for discrete periods of time with remission in between.

✦ *There has never been a manic or hypomanic episode, and the symptoms are not better explained by another disorder including cyclothymia.*

Cyclothymia was covered in the chapter on bipolar and related disorders; it involves mood highs and lows that are not as extreme as those seen in bipolar disorder.

✦ *The symptoms are not due to the direct effect of a drug or medical condition.*

✦ *The symptoms "cause clinically significant distress or impairment in social, occupational, or other important areas of functioning."*

People with high levels of neuroticism as a personality trait may experience persistent low mood, but persistent depressive disorder is different in that it involves a more significant impact on overall functioning.

Persistent depressive disorder may occur on its own or in combination with major depressive disorder, which is sometimes referred to as "double depression". If someone were to meet the diagnostic criteria for a major depressive episode for greater than 2 years, they would be diagnosed with both major depressive disorder and persistent depressive disorder. Depressive episodes may also occur intermittently throughout a period of persistent depressive disorder.

The low mood experienced by people with persistent depressive disorder may be longstanding, and they will sometimes report feeling as though they've always been depressed. The degree of overall functional impairment can be the same or higher than what's found in major depressive disorder.

The annual prevalence of persistent depressive disorder in the United States is around 2%. It begins relatively early in life, either in childhood, adolescence, or early adulthood. Parental loss or separation in childhood can increase the risk of developing this disorder.

Ashley L Peterson

Dissociative Disorders

Dissociation occurs on a spectrum ranging from normal human experience to pathological. "Normal" dissociation is the kind of thing that happens when you return home on autopilot and have no memory of how you got there. Dissociation can be an adaptive survival mechanism during highly traumatic events. Dissociation becomes pathological when it persists well after it is no longer adaptive, and it is much more extreme and far less influenced by conscious control compared to "normal" experiences of dissociation.

A particularly extreme but rare form is dissociative identity disorder, sometimes referred to as multiple personality disorder. Depersonalization/derealization disorder is another form of dissociative disorder that's covered in this chapter. Dissociative symptoms may also occur in the context of various other conditions, including PTSD and borderline personality disorder, but the disorders in this chapter involve dissociation as the primary feature of the illness.

❋ ❋ ❋

Dissociative Identity Disorder (DID)

The diagnostic criteria for dissociative identity disorder are:

✦ *There are disruptions in identity with the existence of at least two separate personalities. There is a subjective sense of separateness of the personalities and limited ability of each personality to control the others. There are differences in feeling, behaviour, awareness, memory, perception, and/or thinking among the different personalities.*

> This is the fundamental feature of DID, and involves entirely separate personalities rather than multiple facets to the same personality as many "normal" people experience. When one alternate personality assumes control, other personalities may be entirely dissociated, or they may be aware of the speech or actions of their body but feel that they have no control over it.

✦ *There are significant memory gaps.*

Following dissociative experiences in which an alter personality has been "front", there may be gaps in memory of that time period while other personality disorders are dissociated. These aren't minor memory lapses, but rather extended amounts of time or significant events that are missing.

✦ *The symptoms cause "clinically significant distress or impairment in social, occupational, or other important areas of functioning."*

✦ *The experiences are not consistent with cultural/religious beliefs or practices.*

In some cultures or religious traditions, "possession" may be seen as a culturally normative experience, in which case a diagnosis of DID would generally not be appropriate. However, that's not to say it would be impossible for someone within these groups to develop pathological dissociative experiences.

✦ *The symptoms aren't due to the direct effects of a drug or medical condition.*

While the list of symptoms is not lengthy, careful evaluation is required to be certain that this is the correct diagnosis. Because this illness is quite rare, many mental health professionals are not experienced in treating it. In my 15 years as a mental health nurse I have never encountered a patient with diagnosed DID in the context of my work.

The different personality states may vary in how overtly they are present. This is influenced by a number of factors, including stress, culture, and internal dynamics. The DSM-5 describes "possession-form cases" of DID, which tend to involve very overt identity disruptions and a sense that an outside being has taken control. There may be sustained identity disruptions during periods of significant environmental stress as the system struggles to cope.

People with DID may experience multiple independent streams of thought/voices that they feel unable to control. They may have sudden surges of thoughts or feelings that do not feel like their own and may be inconsistent with how they would typically think/feel. Different alters may have different genders, preferences, and beliefs.

There may be gaps in memories of important events over the course of the person's life, including lapses in well-established memories like how to perform routine tasks. People may discover evidence that they've done something without having any recollection of doing it, or find themselves somewhere with no idea of how they got there.

Many people with DID experience flashbacks, which may involve a switch of identity. The person may be unable to remember the flashback immediately afterwards.

The vast majority of individuals with DID have a history of significant trauma early in life, with different personalities developing to serve particular survival functions. The first overt identity disruptions may occur when the person is removed from the traumatic environment, when there are later traumatic experiences, or when their abuser dies or becomes seriously ill.

Common co-occurring conditions include depression, anxiety, addictions, and non-epileptic seizures. There may be transient psychotic symptoms. Self-harm and suicidal behaviour are common, with over 70% of people with DID attempting suicide at least once.

�※　　꧑　　꧑

Depersonalization/Derealization Disorder (DPDR)

Depersonalization and derealization are two forms of dissociation. Both may be experienced by people who do not have depersonalization/derealization disorder, and a separate diagnosis of DPDR would not be given if another diagnosis better accounted for the symptoms.

The diagnostic criteria for depersonalization/derealization disorder are:

✦ *There are persistent, repeated experiences of depersonalization and/or derealization:*

> The idea here is that these are not occasional isolated experiences, but rather symptoms that are ongoing on a regular basis.

- *Depersonalization: a sense of unreality and being outside oneself with regards to thoughts, feelings, and body*

> This is a sense of detachment from the self, or a feeling that parts of the self are not familiar. An individual may feel as though they have no self at all. Emotions and thoughts may be noticed but only in a detached, impersonal way. Bodily sensations may feel foreign. Speech and movements may feel unnatural and automated. Sometimes people will report an out-of-body type of experience where the body is seen from a detached perspective, such as being viewed from above.

- *Derealization: a sense of unreality and being detached from one's surroundings, while elements of the environment may appear dreamlike or distorted*

    The individual may feel like they're in a fog, or as though there is some sort of barrier separating them from the surrounding world. Objects in the environment may be perceived as fake or lifeless. There may be alterations in visual perceptions or distortions in sounds.

✦ *During these episodes, the individual is able to distinguish reality from unreality.*

    This criterion is to differentiate dissociation from psychosis. With psychosis, unreal elements are perceived as entirely real, whereas in depersonalization and derealization there is a sense of recognition that what's perceived is reality, although it feels unreal.

✦ *The symptoms result in "clinically significant distress or impairment in social, occupational, or other important areas of functioning."*

    Like any serious mental illness, this condition has a significant impact on functioning that goes far beyond the occasional autopilot trip home that would be considered "normal".

✦ *The symptoms are not due to the direct effects of a drug or medical condition, and are not better accounted for by another mental disorder.*

    Depersonalization and derealization can both happen in the context of other mental illnesses, so it's important that the diagnosis that's given is the one that best captures the complete picture of symptoms experienced.

Often people with this disorder have difficulty describing how they're feeling and understanding exactly what it is that they're experiencing. They may wonder if they have some form of brain damage, and may report vague odd feelings in the head. There may be a distorted sense of time, and memories may feel foreign. There may be significant rumination over whether or not things are real. Some anxious and depressive symptoms are common. Physical reactivity to emotions may be decreased, and there may be a lack of facial expressiveness.

The average age of onset is 16 years old. A history of childhood trauma is common. Around 1/3 of people with the disorder have clearly delineated episodes or depersonalization/

derealization with symptom-free time interspersed, another 1/3 experience continuous symptoms, and the other 1/3 begin with discrete episodes that end up evolving over time into continuous symptoms. Symptoms may worsen in response to triggers like stress, worsening mood symptoms, poor sleep, or overstimulating environments.

❄ ❄ ❄

Elle Rose's Story (Depersonalization/Derealization Disorder)

When you wake up in the morning, a separation occurs between sleep and your waking life. You can feel it, but you don't really need to – most people know when this happens, when they split from their dreaming life from their waking life, and the difference is very distinct. When I wake up in the morning, the area between waking and dreaming doesn't quite separate the way that it should – instead I feel sort of stuck between waking and dreaming, all the time. I go about my day, do my makeup, watch some television, talk to people, but I often feel like I'm either watching myself from above or from beside myself as I talk to people and go about my day.

Other times, I look down at my hands, and wonder if I even have bones in my hands – and then I think I'm actually losing my mind. One of the strangest things about this disorder is feeling as if you're on the brink of losing your mind, constantly, but never quite completely losing it. Dissociation is not the same as psychosis, but when dissociation becomes severe, you can begin to feel like you're inching towards a psychotic break, but you never do, which can make it quite confusing. It feels like you're in a dream, or like everyone is dreaming of you, and you aren't quite sure what's happening. I try to ignore it, which so far seems to be the best strategy I've come up with, but it's still there more often than not, as I sit outside of myself, watching the situation, wondering how long I can pretend I'm not watching what I'm doing while I'm doing it.

As Tweedledee told Alice when she went to wake the king, "Well, it's no use your talking about waking him when you're one of the things in his dream. You know very well you're not real." Alice insists she is real. I often feel like Alice – tumbling down the rabbit hole, falling through the looking glass – but unlike her, I haven't felt the difference between waking and dreaming since I first began to struggle with this. I have hope, to a point, for recovery, but my focus now is more on figuring out how to live without it bothering or impairing me. Some days are pretty bad. But more often than not, as I continue dealing with it, the days are getting better.

– *Elle Rose, Secretladyspider*

Feeding and Eating Disorders

It's worth keeping in mind that regardless of the specific diagnosis, these illnesses are eating disorders, not weight disorders. An eating disorder can be present regardless of a person's body size or shape. Weight does not accurately reflect the underlying problem, that there is a fundamentally disordered relationship with food and more importantly with the body. While eating disorders are often thought of as female conditions, they occur in both men and women.

The diagnosis of unspecified feeding or eating disorder would be used for someone who doesn't fit exactly into any of the other diagnoses. Other DSM-5 diagnoses that won't be covered here include binge-eating disorder and pica, which involves eating non-nutritive substances.

Anorexia Nervosa

The word anorexia on its own refers simply to loss of appetite, and may be used to describe effects of other illnesses or a medication side effect. Anorexia nervosa refers specifically to the eating disorder.

The diagnostic criteria for anorexia nervosa are:

✦ *There is restricted caloric intake that is insufficient to meet bodily requirements, leading to significantly low body weight.*

> The evaluation of low body weight is based on age, gender, and physical health. The World Health Organization and the U.S. Centers For Disease Control have established a body mass index (BMI) of 18.5 as the lower limit of a healthy body weight for adults. BMI is calculated using height in metres divided by body weight in kilograms squared. For children and adolescents the determination of significantly low body weight is more complex than just calculating BMI.

✦ *There is an intense fear of weight gain or becoming fat despite being at a low weight, and this is accompanied by active attempts to interfere with weight gain.*

> Losing further weight does nothing to ease these fears. There would never be a "thin enough" to alleviate worries about body shape and size. There is strong resistance to any attempts made by others to promote gain weight, and intensive supervision may be required to ensure adequate intake.

✦ *There is a disturbance in the experience of one's own body shape, excessive focus on body size/shape with respect to evaluating the self, or enduring failure to recognize the risks associated with the current low body weight.*

> The individual's conception of their body size and shape differs considerably from objective reality. The concerns about shape/weight may be focused on the body as a whole, or especially directed towards particular areas that are thought to be too fat. The person may frequently weigh themselves or closely examine their body to monitor for weight gain or areas that may be deemed too large. Weight loss tends to be viewed positively as an indication of self-discipline and control, while weight gain is seen as an unacceptable sign of weakness. Often the individual is unable to recognize the potential for significant medical consequences as a result of the disordered eating, even with profoundly low weight.

The diagnosis may be specified as restricting type or binge-eating/purging type, which involves self-induced vomiting and other purging methods such as the misuse of laxatives or diuretics. There may be an absence of binging, with just purging behaviours. Restricting can involve restriction of intake or increased caloric expenditure by exercising heavily. At different points of the illness an individual may experience both of these subtypes, so when this diagnostic specifier is used, it refers only to the current pattern at the time of assessment.

Severity is specified based on body mass index, but this may be altered to reflect clinical symptoms, overall disability, and level of supervision required.

- **mild**: BMI $\geq$ 17 kg/m^2
- **moderate**: BMI 16-16.99 kg/m^2
- **severe**: BMI 15-15.99 kg/m^2
- **extreme**: BMI < 15 kg/m^2

Significant physical health consequences may result from anorexia nervosa. Due to the effects of the disorder on sex hormones, females with this condition will often stop menstruating. The heart is made up largely of muscle, and when there is extreme muscle loss this can cause abnormalities in cardiac functioning, including changes in heart rate and blood pressure. Bone density losses can occur and may not be fully reversible. Fine, downy hair called lanugo may grow on the skin.

Sometimes medications are misused in an attempt to lose more weight. Insulin-dependent diabetics may skip insulin doses so their bodies are unable to metabolize carbohydrates, which can result in dangerously high blood sugars.

Other mental health effects associated with anorexia nervosa include depressed mood, social withdrawal, irritability, and insomnia. There may be obsessions and compulsions, often related to food. There is often a strong desire for control, and a lack of flexibility in thought patterns. There may be impulsive behaviours, and an increased risk of substance abuse. Suicide risk is also elevated.

Anorexia nervosa occurs in around 0.4% of young females each year, and is more common in high income countries. It is approximately ten times more common in females than males. Onset is usually during adolescence or young adulthood.

❄ ❄ ❄

Paula's Story (Anorexia Nervosa)

I was a fat child and was reminded of it constantly by other children. Thank God there was no social media then, or I would never have gotten a break from their cruelty. My parents had terrible eating habits, which they passed along to me, until I rebelled at age 11. When I began high school, I was 5'4" and 108 pounds, but I felt I needed to stay constantly vigilant. I volunteered as a lab assistant and skipped lunch break.

Soon, I became ill with a strep infection and was hospitalized for a few days. By the time I was discharged, I weighed under 100 pounds. My mother took me shopping for new clothes because mine were falling off. My parents began expressing concern at my weight loss, but it was winter in Illinois, so I bundled up in thick sweaters. That kept the comments at bay. I kept losing weight deliberately though, scaring myself when I dropped to 95. I decided that was enough and I'd stay right there.

I wasn't sure exactly how many calories I needed to maintain 95 pounds, so I erred on the side of caution and chose 1150 per day and kept track religiously, writing down every bite in a notebook. If my pen slipped, I began a new notebook. I decided I should exercise twice a day too. I jumped rope obsessively, and if I missed a step, I made myself start again. Soon, my weight dropped to the low 90s. I fainted while babysitting one afternoon, which was scary. Dizziness became my new normal. I began cooking for my parents in a bid to stave off my mother making food for me. Then I would pretend to eat a plateful before they got home and just have a little "more" with them. I liked watching other people eat and judging them as gluttons, while at the same time envying them for being able to enjoy food because I no longer could. I ate in minuscule bites to make food last as long as possible, even when I was starving. I thought about food constantly and dreamt about it too.

By the time summer came around I was 90 pounds. My periods had disappeared. Then people noticed, since I wore lighter clothing. They weren't horrified however—most of the other girls expressed jealousy at my slenderness. My parents were concerned and sent me to counsellors, but these were the same counsellors they used for marital help. They didn't home in on my unusual eating habits; it was more general chatting about family dynamics.

Late summer, we went on vacation to California. My parents were not getting along. As they yelled at each other, I brushed my hair in the hotel room and watched it fall out on the floor in a ray of sunlight. I was down to 87 pounds. And I knew I would die if I did not stop. That night I ate some steak. And I sat in the front seat of the rental car like a baby, curled up next to my mommy. I cried. I did not want to die. I was 16 years old.

– *Paula Light, Light Motifs II*

Bulimia Nervosa

Contrary to the common misconception that people with eating disorders are always thin, most people with bulimia nervosa have a BMI that's in the normal to overweight range (18.5-30). This is a particularly strong example of how eating disorders are about one's relationship with food and the body, not about weight.

The diagnostic criteria for bulimia nervosa are:

✦ *There are recurrent binge eating episodes, which involve both of:*
  • *Eating, within a 2-hour or less period, an amount of food that's considerably larger than what most people would eat in the same circumstances*

Of course this is quite subjective, but the idea here is to differentiate illness-related behaviour from the "normal", more voluntary and controllable chowing down one might do during a big family holiday dinner.

- *A feeling that the eating is out of control*

   This lack of control is an essential part of the diagnosis, and is another way of differentiating binging from "normal" overeating. This is not a willing choice to binge, but an urge that seems impossible to control. Some people will experience this loss of control in the form of a dissociative-like experience, causing them to become detached from the actual binging behaviour.

✦ *There are recurrent attempts to compensate for the binging in order to not gain weight. This may include self-induced vomiting, misuse of medications, fasting, or exercising excessively.*

   Vomiting is the most common purging method, and people with the illness become increasingly adept at inducing vomiting to the point that they may be able to vomit spontaneously without any sort of stimulus. Laxatives are one example of medications that may be misused. Regardless of the specific compensatory method used, purging can cause significant medical consequences.

✦ *The binging and purging happen at least once a week on average for a period of 3 months.*

   This criterion helps to establish a clear pattern of illness rather than something that may be transient and stress-related.

✦ *There is an overemphasis on body shape and weight in determining self-worth and self-esteem.*

   In many cultures a heavy emphasis is placed on body shape and size in determining one's attractiveness and value in society. This criterion goes beyond that, and involves a degree of importance placed on body shape and size that runs far deeper than would be considered culturally normative.

✦ *The symptoms don't occur only during episodes of anorexia nervosa.*

   This criterion is to differentiate from anorexia nervosa, binging/purging type.

Severity specifiers are based on the frequency of engaging in inappropriate compensatory behaviours, not on the frequency of binging. The severity may be adjusted depending on the impact of other symptoms and effects on overall functioning:

- **mild**: on average 1-3 episodes per week
- **moderate**: on average 4-7 episodes per week
- **severe**: on average 8-13 episodes per week
- **extreme**: on average 14 or more episodes per week

There is no particular type of food that's necessarily involved in binging, although often the foods consumed are those that the individual would normally avoid. Binges may be triggered by a variety of factors including low mood, interpersonal stressors, or boredom. People with this disorder will often attempt to hide their binging and purging symptoms out of a sense of shame. Between binges, caloric intake is often restricted.

Medications may be misused to try to prevent weight gain, including thyroid hormones or insulin. Purging can result in electrolyte disturbances (sodium, potassium, etc.) which can have serious medical consequences, including disturbance in cardiac functioning. There may also be damage to the stomach or esophagus from repeated vomiting. Muscle damage can occur, and this can affect cardiac muscle, leading to abnormal heart rhythms.

People who use laxatives to purge may become dependent on them in order to have a bowel movement. As with anorexia nervosa, females with bulimia nervosa often have menstrual irregularities or the cessation of periods altogether. Mood and anxiety symptoms are common, and there is an increased risk of suicide.

Bulimia nervosa is about three times more common than anorexia nervosa, occurring in about 1-1.5% of young females each year. Like anorexia nervosa, bulimia nervosa is about ten times more common in females than males. Onset is usually in adolescence or early adulthood.

✻ ✻ ✻

Caz's Story (Bulimia Nervosa)

When I was 13, I developed bulimia. It started, initially, as a means to rid myself of occasional meals as I'd been struggling with worries over my weight, size and body shape. It quickly became more than the odd meals, and soon grew to binge eating large quantities before purging. It became about self-comfort, self-loathing and control, but I was scared I wasn't in control any more, so I spoke to my GP. I expected the diagnosis because I knew that purging 'regular' meals was bulimia, though I hadn't realized at the time that the binge/purge cycle also came under this diagnosis. I was scared and embarrassed seeking help and had no idea what to expect as I hadn't confided in anyone else.

My diagnosis seemed fairly straightforward based on my account of my behaviours, though my GP didn't pick up on the depression or anxiety that partly fuelled the bulimia until a few years later. The response I received wasn't compassionate, nor was it too negative, but it felt somewhat judgemental and cold. I didn't get the sense of support that I had hoped for.

I was sent to counselling that did more harm than good, with a therapist who admitted she knew next to nothing about eating disorders. These days, there are more professional services and well-trained staff, so I'd hope diagnosis could open doors to the proper support people need. I hadn't realized at the time that bulimia would forever be on my record like a black mark against my name. When I developed health issues age 19 unrelated to my previous history of bulimia, this mental health diagnosis was used against me and referred to at times in order to fob me off. Again, I hope this has changed a little in recent years to prevent such discrimination, even though there's a long way to go in that regard. Having a label at first made me feel that it was part of my identity, that I was in effect "just a girl with an eating disorder." It took a while for me to see the diagnosis as a challenge I survived and grew stronger because of facing it in my life.

I overcame bulimia when I took a more radical approach that I'd read about in a self-help book of acknowledging and accepting that it may be a part of my life in some form for the foreseeable future; as long as the underlying thoughts were at the back of my subconscious and I wasn't acting on them or letting them dictate my life, I would survive. This did away with the all-or-nothing, black and white thinking, and the regular "it's the last time" binges. I don't think my brain will be symptom-free as the likes of calorie counting become hardwired and I still struggle with control issues and perfectionism at times, but I've been free of physical bulimia in the years since. Recovery for me has meant working on self-compassion, coping strategies, and healing, which is a continual work-in-progress for myself as it is for most of us as perfectly imperfect human beings.

– *Caz, Invisibly Me*

Ashley L Peterson

Gender Dysphoria

With the release of the DSM-5, there was a change in name from gender identity disorder to gender dysphoria. Personally I like this change, as it starts to shift the "problem" away from an individual's self-identification and onto the profound distress that can result from having an identity that's often considered to be very much outside of societal norms. The current diagnostic label seems to be a change in a positive direction that's a little bit more consistent with what's seen in societies where a third gender exists. In these social groups, identification with the third gender construct is not necessarily a source of any distress as it is a socially accepted type of identity.

There are a few terms that should be defined in relation to sex and gender:

- **Biological sex**: This is determined based on the primary and secondary sex characteristics, which are determined by genetics (X and Y chromosomes). Primary sex characteristics are the reproductive organs that are present at birth, while secondary sex characteristics are those that develop at puberty, such as breasts.

- **Gender identity**: This refers to the social gender constructs that an individual subjectively identifies with, e.g. male, female, non-binary, or other queer identities.

  - **Experienced gender identity**: This is an individual's inner experience in relation to social gender constructs.

  - **Expressed gender identity**: This is the outward expression of gender, including clothing and grooming. It may or may not be congruent with an individual's experienced gender identity or biological sex.

- **Assigned gender**: For DSM purposes, this refers to the natal gender, i.e. the gender assigned at birth. Sometimes this is a simple match to biological sex, but in the case of individuals born with ambiguous primary sex characteristics it may be selected by parents and/or medical professionals.

There are some differences in the criteria for children and adults, but here we will cover the adult/adolescent criteria. The criteria for gender dysphoria are:

✦ *There is a marked incongruence between the individual's gender identity and the assigned gender, lasting 6 months or more, with at least 2 of the following:*

As already mentioned the assigned gender typically refers to the gender at birth. Incongruence may involve identifying as the opposite gender, non-binary, or other gender queer identities. The six-month time-frame is used in adults/adolescents to distinguish from more transient disruptions in gender identity.

- *A marked incongruence between one's gender identity and the primary or secondary characteristics associated with the biological sex*
- *A strong wish not to have one's possessed biological sex characteristics due to their incongruence with the experienced gender identity*

  As an example, a biologically male individual who identifies as female may have a strong wish not to have a penis because it does not fit with their female identity.

- *A strong wish to have those biological sex characteristics associated with the gender the individual identifies with*

  A biologically male individual may have a strong wish to have breasts in order to be consistent with their female gender identity.

- *A strong wish to be of a gender other than the assigned gender*
- *A strong wish to be treated by others in a manner consistent with the gender the individual identifies with*

  This criterion touches on the very social element of being in a gendered-incongruent body.

- *A strong wish to have the sorts of feelings that would normally be associated with the gender identified with*

  Social gender constructs tend to be associated with certain emotions and forms of emotional expression, and a person with gender dysphoria would feel a stronger connection to the emotions associated with their gender identity. As an example, a trans female may wish to be able to experience and express sadness in the manner that is socially acceptable/expected for women.

✦ *"The condition is associated with clinically significant distress or impairment in social, occupational, or other areas of functioning."*

This distress and functional impairment comes not so much from the gender identity itself but rather the incongruence between that identity and societal expectations.

Specifiers that may be applied to this diagnosis are:

- **with a disorder of sex development**: congenital disorders affecting sex hormones and sex characteristics may affect an individual's experience of gender
- **post-transition**: the individual is living full-time in their identified gender and has accessed some type of medical support in the form of hormones or surgery

Between the age of 2-4 years children tend to start behaving in a manner associated with their gender, and it is around this age that cross-gender behaviours may first be observed. Gender dysphoria persists into adolescence/adulthood in up to 50% of individuals with early cross-gender behaviour, although there is considerable variability in these rates. Gender dysphoria is considered late onset when it begins around puberty or later.

The discrepancy between identified and assigned gender may result in a range of different behaviours that tend to be influenced by age group.

The extent to which gender expression matches gender identity may vary. When gender expression differs from what is expected of an individual's natal gender (e.g. a girl who is a "tomboy"), that alone does not signify gender dysphoria.

Gender dysphoria is associated with an increased risk of suicide, and this may persist even following gender reassignment. There is significant stigma associated with being transgendered, which contributes to an increased risk for other mental health conditions as well as lower socioeconomic status.

Neurodevelopmental Disorders

ADHD, autism spectrum disorder, and tic disorders all fall under the umbrella of neurodevelopmental disorders. These involve patterns of symptoms that emerge during the developmental years, regardless of whether they end up being diagnosed in childhood or adulthood.

This group of diagnoses also includes intellectual disabilities and learning disorders, although they won't be covered in this chapter.

❈ ❈ ❈

Attention-Deficit/Hyperactivity Disorder (ADHD)

What was formerly known as attention deficit disorder (ADD) is now called attention deficit/hyperactivity disorder (ADHD). ADHD inattentive type is used to describe people with attention deficits but no hyperactivity. While ADHD is commonly thought of as a disorder that's mostly found in children, it doesn't simply disappear after the teen years. However, the hyperactivity symptoms are often better controlled once a person reaches adulthood.

While it may seem at first glance to be paradoxical that people with ADHD are given stimulant medications, there's actually a good explanation for it. The prefrontal cortex region of the brain is responsible for executive functioning. It acts kind of like an air traffic control centre for higher level thought processes. If someone's cognitive air traffic controllers are asleep on the job, figurative planes are flying any which way and crashing into each other. Stimulant medications get those mental air traffic controllers back to work and focused so the planes can start flying in a more orderly fashion.

The diagnostic criteria for ADHD are:

✦ *There is a persistent pattern of inattention and/or hyperactivity that has a negative impact on functioning/development, with one of:*

The persistent pattern and impact on functioning/development are important in distinguishing from "normal" patterns that would be expected from someone at the same stage of development.

- _Inattention_: at least 6 of the following lasting for at least 6 months, which are not expected for the developmental stage and have a negative impact on functioning:
  - ‣ Problems with attention to detail and careless mistakes in activities like work/school

    To be considered pathological the frequency and severity of the inattention must be significantly greater than what would "normally" be experienced by someone of that age and level of development.

  - ‣ Problems maintaining attention

    This poses challenges for activities requiring sustained attention such as listening to others speak, engaging in a conversation, or reading.

  - ‣ Does not seem to listen when someone is speaking to them directly

    The person may appear to be distracted even when there is no apparent reason for the distraction.

  - ‣ Does not follow through on tasks, and gets sidetracked easily

    Starting a task may not be a problem, but focus is quickly lost and the task does not end up getting completed.

  - ‣ Problems with organizing and sequencing tasks

    This can include poor time management and messiness.

  - ‣ Tends to avoid tasks that involve sustained attention, or dislikes them when forced to do such tasks
  - ‣ Easily loses important, basic items

    In a child this might be school-related items, or in an adult it might be things like house keys.

> *Easily distracted by unrelated stimuli*

This can be especially problematic in situations where there are high levels of environmental stimuli from multiple sources.

> *Forgetful in usual activities*

This isn't a memory problem per se, but rather lapses in attention that occur while carrying out activities.

- *Hyperactivity/impulsivity: at least 6 of the following lasting for at least 6 months, which are not expected for the developmental stage and have a negative impact on functioning:*
  > *Fidgeting*
  > *Getting up when expected to stay seated*
  > *Running/climbing when it's not appropriate to do so*

Adolescents and adults may not outwardly engage in this type of behaviour, but instead describe a sense of restlessness.

  > *Unable to remain quiet while engaging in leisure activities*
  > *Seem to always be moving, unable to be still for long*
  > *Talking excessively*
  > *Interrupting questions to blurt out an answer*
  > *Problems waiting for others to go first*
  > *Interrupts others' activities/conversations*

✦ *Several of the symptoms were present before age 12.*

It's helpful to get information from caregivers in establishing a clear picture for this.

✦ *Several of the symptoms occur in multiple settings.*

This may include home, school, and/or work. The extent of symptoms and prominence of particular symptoms may vary from setting to setting.

✦ *The symptoms clearly interfere with overall functioning.*

The symptoms are not better accounted for by another mental disorder.

The disorder may be specified as predominantly inattentive, predominantly hyperactive/impulsive, or combined. Individuals with ADHD may struggle with low frustration tolerance, irritability, or quickly changeable moods. There is also an increased risk of suicide attempts associated with ADHD.

Symptoms of ADHD begin to clearly emerge usually starting at around 4 years old. The hyperactivity tends to decrease as the individual moves into adolescence and adulthood, but the attention symptoms often persist. ADHD is more common in males than females. In females, it tends to be the attention symptoms that predominate rather than the hyperactive symptoms.

Casey's Story (ADHD)

I was diagnosed with Attention Deficit Disorder (ADD) almost a year ago, at the age of 30. Out of the handful of diagnoses I've received, ADD was the one that blew my mind. At first, I couldn't understand the diagnosis.

Sure, I had a problem with concentrating but I got decent grades growing up. I had a college reading level in third grade. I was in band and even on the high school newspaper. I also got accepted into a good state university for journalism.

Despite mostly good grades, I didn't pay much attention in class unless it was a class like creative writing, English, or literature.

An engaging class about the written word always enticed me into the world of fiction, personal essays, and poetry. It was a land of hope and different realities that took me away from the harshness of my home.

In any other class, no matter how hard I tried, I couldn't concentrate. I would daydream or write poetry throughout class. I wasn't hyper, I was just always lost in my mind and constant flighty thoughts.

At home, I couldn't study. No matter how hard I tried, I just couldn't concentrate. I'd open a textbook but the words I read would immediately slip out of my brain, as if I hadn't read anything at all. I had a million other thoughts swarming around my brain, like working bees around their queen.

It was like an old western quick draw between what I read and my other thoughts and my other thoughts always won (and still do).

On the other end of the ADD spectrum, I would hyper-fixate on my own little projects. I'd write all day, poetry, stories, and even lists. All the while, listening to music and writing alphabetical lists of songs I loved.

I'd play video games for hours and hours at a time. I'd read a chapter of a book, bookmark it, move on to a second book, read a chapter, move on to the next book. I'd have piles of books that I was reading at once. I was an oddity.

When I got to college, school wasn't as easy to pass without effort. Between anxiety, bipolar depression, and undiagnosed ADD, I was failing. I'd sit in my dorm room all day, catching Pokemon, instead of studying or going to class.

I'm a college dropout three times over.

Working retail my entire 20s, ADD moved me up the corporate ladder. I could multitask so well that I could stock most of the store, greet customers, and work on the register as the only person in the store.

I was (I've been sober for 4 years) also a methamphetamine addict. Before when I tried meth, it was like I could focus for the first time in my life, no matter how daunting or boring the task before me was.

Of course, the negatives of addiction outweighed any of the perceived benefits.

ADD had snuck up on me, grabbed a hold of my brain, and I was none the wiser.

With the help of a psychiatrist and therapist, I'm finally getting the help I've needed since childhood. I'm working on conquering all my demons, including my inattention, my constant lack of focus, and my need for multitasking.

It's a continuous battle that I'm fighting and so many others are fighting. Apparently, it's quite common for females to be diagnosed later in life because they were able to mask their troubles throughout school.

As I write this, I'm watching Stranger Things and I have five tabs open, from my e-mail to an article about seahorses. This is what ADD is like for me.

Ashley L Peterson

—*Casey Elizabeth Dennis, This Bipolar Brat*

❄ ❄ ❄

Autism Spectrum Disorder

Autism and Asperger's syndrome used to be two distinct diagnoses, but in the current version of the DSM the two have been merged into autism spectrum disorder (ASD). The DSM-5 takes a symptom/illness-based view, while many in the autism community would argue that autism is a difference in relating to the world rather than an illness. This section will only cover the DSM-5 interpretation.

The diagnostic criteria for autism spectrum disorder are:

✦ *There are persistent deficits across multiple types of social interactions, as shown by:*

• *Deficits in reciprocal interactions, both socially and emotionally*

> There may be difficulties with using language in a reciprocal way during social interaction, including sharing thoughts and feelings with others. There may be problems imitating the behaviour of others in situations where this would be called for, and initiation of social interaction may be limited. In general there is a lack of "normal" social intuition as to what is or is not socially appropriate. More complex social cues are often particularly challenging, such as determining when to enter a conversation or whether something is appropriate to say in a particular situation.

• *Deficits in nonverbal social cues, including facial expression, eye contact, and gestures*

> The individual's pattern of eye contact does not fit with cultural norms, and there may be a lack of typical facial expressions, gestures, and vocal intonation. Body language may appear odd. Certain behaviours like following someone's gaze or looking where they are pointing may seem unnatural to someone with autism.

• *Deficits in navigating relationships and adjusting behaviour based on the particular social context*

> This criterion must be considered in the context of culture and age-appropriate norms. There is often reduced social interest. There may be difficulties

understanding why different behaviours are expected in different contexts, and there is often a lack of awareness regarding reciprocity in social relationships.

✦ *There are repetitive, rigid patterns, with at least 2 of the following:*

• *Repetitive movements or vocalizations*

This is sometimes referred to as stimming. Repetitive movements may include hand flapping or finger flicking. There may also be repetitive use of objects, vocal echoing, or repetition of certain words/phrases.

• *Inflexibility in routines and behaviour, with distress resulting from deviations in those routines*

Even small deviations from what is expected can produce strong reactions. The individual may insist on strictly following established patterns, which may include firm food restrictions.

• *Hyper-focused, fixated interests*

These are abnormal in intensity and/or the amount of time devoted to them.

• *Either over- or under-reactive to sensory stimulation*

This may pertain to stimulation in any of the five senses, with variability depending on the individual. Some people may be hypersensitive to certain types of light, while others may feel bombarded by auditory stimuli.

✦ *Symptoms need to be present during the early developmental years.*

As the individual gets older they may learn to mask, so symptom presentation may change over time. Autism spectrum disorder may be diagnosed in adulthood, but because it's considered a developmental disorder, the symptoms must have begun during earlier developmental stages.

✦ *Symptoms cause "clinically significant impairment in social, occupational, or other important areas of current functioning."*

The age at which this impairment may appear is variable depending on the individual and the characteristics of their environment.

✦ *The symptoms are not better accounted for by an intellectual disability.*

Possible specifiers that may be added to an ASD diagnosis include:

- **with/without intellectual impairment:** In those with high intelligence, there may be a significant gap between intellectual and functional abilities.

- **with/without language impairment:** Speech impairments can range from being nonverbal to language delays to echoing of speech. Language may be stilted or overly literal.

- **with catatonia:** Catatonia is described in detail in the chapter on psychotic disorders

Severity specifiers ranging from mild to severe reflect the extent of difficulties with social communication and repetitive behaviours, as well as the level of support required for functioning.

The key feature of autism spectrum disorder is persistent impairment in reciprocal social communication and interaction. The impairments are sustained and occur across multiple contexts. Sharing thoughts and feelings is difficult, and there is a lack of initiation of social contact.

When making the diagnosis it's useful to have multiple sources of information to draw upon, including caregivers and teachers. Standardized diagnostic tools can be helpful in making an accurate diagnosis.

Autism occurs in around 1% of the population, and is four times more common in males than females. Symptoms often begin to appear between age 12-24 months. Initial symptoms tend to involve delays in language development and lack of social interest/interaction. There is often some improvement in symptoms in adolescence as more compensatory mechanisms are learned.

Luftmentsch's Story (Autism Spectrum Disorder)

Being on the autism spectrum impacts my life in a number of ways. Although I was a high achiever at school, I have always struggled with social and emotional interactions. I struggle to build friendships and relationships and navigating the workplace is a lot harder than I expected. I'm a bit of a loner, so to some extent I don't mind this, but I would like to be more social than I am and to get married one day and I worry if these things are possible for me. I certainly struggle to know how to respond to other people's emotions. Once when I was a child we were on holiday and I was sleeping in a bed under a low rafter. My Mum hit her head badly saying good night to me and I didn't know what to do. She said I should have just hugged her, but that did not occur to me.

I am often unsure when to speak and when to be silent in conversations, particularly when I'm in a group. I also struggle to end conversations, not knowing if it has finished. Similarly, non-verbal communication is very hard. Growing up I avoided making eye contact until my parents noticed. Since then I have tried to make eye contact, but I have to consciously think about when to look and when to look away. I can't do it intuitively.

For a long time I thought I didn't "stim" i.e. make repetitive movements. Eventually I realized I do stim, just fairly subtly, shaking my legs and feet and stroking my face. I like to feel light pressure too, leaning against walls or lightly trapping my fingers in my desk drawer. I also fidget a lot. This all feels vaguely "wrong" and I've never worked out why. It's possible someone told me off for doing it as a child, as often happens to autistic children.

Sensory sensitivity (too much or too little) is a major issue for many autistic people. This can affect different individuals in very different ways. My main problem is being unable to filter out background noise. I can usually tune out consistent background noise (I used to live by a busy road and didn't have trouble with that), but I can't concentrate if people are talking near me as my brain tries to tune in to what they are saying. I used to hate eating in the garden as a child and I think some of that may have been sensory sensitivity to the light shining off our white garden table.

Like many autistic people I have poor executive function, meaning I am very indecisive and struggle to multitask or plan effectively. I like routines and dislike change. If change is forced on me, I do adapt quite quickly, but I resist it beforehand. I am wary of doing new things and going to new places. Anything involving new situations or talking to new people is very scary. As a child I used to ask for detailed advanced descriptions when I was told to do a new thing, particularly regarding interactions with other people and, to be honest, I still do want that advanced warning for things like new jobs. I do hate sudden changes. If someone phones me in the evening, I feel for a long time afterwards that my plans have been changed and everything has gone wrong, just for having to take fifteen minutes out of my time unexpectedly.

Like many autistic people, I have a "special interest," in my case, *Doctor Who*. I know a huge amount of trivia about *Doctor Who* and have a large collection of DVDs and books. My special interest is not just an enjoyable hobby, but also arguably an escape from the world into a fictional world where things are more predictable or controllable.

– Luftmentsch, Vision of the Night

※ ※ ※

Tic Disorders: Tourette's Disorder

The DSM-5 includes three different tic disorder diagnoses: Tourette's disorder, persistent motor or vocal tic disorder, and provisional tic disorder. A tic is defined as "a sudden, rapid, recurrent, nonrhythmic motor movement or vocalization."

The diagnostic criteria for Tourette's disorder, the most severe of the three, are:

✦ *There is the presence of more than one motor tic AND at least one vocal tic at some point in the illness, although they don't have to occur at the same time.*

> A wide range of tics may be displayed. Eye blinking or throat clearing are common. Tics are involuntary, but with effort they can sometimes be suppressed if the individual is able to sense the impending onset of a tic.

> Simple tics, either motor or vocal, are of brief duration and include things like blinking. Complex tics last longer and involve multiple elements. Complex vocal tics may involve repetition of words, including swear words and other inappropriate language, which is known as coprolalia.

✦ *The tics have been present for at least one year, although the frequency may have varied over that time.*

> There may be tic-free periods that last weeks or even months, but at least a year must have passed since the onset of symptoms to be diagnosed.

✦ *The first onset occurs prior to age 18.*

> Because Tourette's is considered a type of developmental disorder, symptoms must first appear during the developmental years.

✦ *The symptoms are not due to the direct effects of a drug or medical condition.*

Multiple tic disorder diagnoses can't be applied at the same time. There is a hierarchy of severity in which Tourette's disorder > persistent motor or vocal tic disorder > provisional tic disorder. If someone is diagnosed with the highest level, Tourette's, that nullifies any previous diagnoses for the other tic disorders.

Tic disorders usually begin before puberty, at around 4-6 years of age on average. Mild tics may not be noticed at a younger age, but may become apparent in hindsight. Symptoms are typically at their most severe around age 10-12 and then decrease with age. Tics tend to be worse during times of stress, anxiety, excitement, or significant fatigue.

Complications during pregnancy have been associated with an increased risk for tic disorders. Males are 2-4 times more likely than females to develop tic disorders. Tic disorders occur in 3-8 per 1000 children of school age.

❄ ❄ ❄

Alice's Story (Tourette's Disorder)

It's like you're possessed by a hyperactive five-year-old boy. It's like you're a puppet being controlled by someone evil. It's like you're a can of Coca-Cola all shaken up and ready to explode. It's like you're trapped in a body you can't control. You are trapped in a body you can't control. That's what Tourette's feels like.

I have, in particular order, stroked a date's face before I even had a chance to introduce myself, called my boss "a little bitch" before running my hands through his beard, told police officers they were "pigs", told a doctor "you don't know what you're doing," and flipped my examiners the bird before blowing them kisses in my final year French oral examination.

But the humour of Tourette's doesn't compensate for the problems which arise with having Tourette's. And there are many, many problems.

It's embarrassing. To my mortification, I once ticced "big face" at a girl. She didn't have a big face. It was nonsensical – as most tics are. Nevertheless, she was hurt. She started crying. It turned out the kids at school used to call her that.

It's uncomfortable. You can suppress tics. Most people with Tourette's do. It's not a nice feeling, though. It kind of feels like you're holding your breath – at some point you're going to exhale.

It hurts. 86 percent of people with Tourette's report having had tics which have caused them pain. I have put my hand through three windows. I have punched walls. I have repeatedly slapped myself across the face.

People stare at you, people laugh at you. Now, as a general rule, this is completely normal and I'm fine with it. If you're doing something weird then people are going to look and laugh at you, and that's OK.

But then there's more than staring and there's more than laughing. When people with Tourette's feature in the media, they will invariably have the swearing variety of the condition, even though the vast majority of people with Tourette's don't swear. Usually it's a program in which the person is trying to get a girlfriend, or a job, or maybe he's just trying to make his way through the airport without saying the word "bomb". These kinds of programs invite you to look at how hard it is for this strange person to do something incredibly ordinary. It's entertainment, a spectacle, it's voyeuristic and I don't like it.

Normally, Tourette's starts in childhood, but I only started ticcing in my early twenties. I was a foreign exchange student in Barcelona, and I couldn't stop opening and closing my mouth, screwing up my eyes. My teacher asked me what I was doing. I said I didn't know. She said it looked like I had tics. She was right.

One year later, I was sitting across from a neurologist. I was effing and blinding, writhing and contorting. He took about five minutes to tell me I had Tourette's, a further five minutes to tell me I'd always have Tourette's, and after a further ten to tell me his advice would be to live my life as though as I didn't have Tourette's.

Good, but impossible advice. Because how do you live life as though you didn't have Tourette's when you have Tourette's?

– *Alice Franklin, How to Have Tourette's*

OCD and Related Disorders

The DSM-5 chapter on obsessive compulsive disorder (OCD) also includes several other related diagnoses. Body dysmorphic disorder involves obsessive thoughts, and often repetitive behaviours as well. Body-focused repetitive behaviour (BFRB) disorders include trichotillomania (hair pulling disorder) and skin excoriation disorder (also known as dermatillomania). The diagnostic criteria for trichotillomania (hair pulling disorder) are included in this chapter, but the criteria are very similar regardless of the specific bodily focus of the repetitive behaviours. Hoarding disorder is included in this section of the DSM-5, but won't be covered in this book.

Obsessive compulsive personality disorder (OCPD) is a type of personality disorder with some similarities to OCD. Perfectionism, rigidity, and need for control are key features of OCPD, and the colloquial characterization of people or behaviours as "so OCD" tends to bear a much greater resemblance to OCPD than OCD.

※　※　※

Obsessive Compulsive Disorder (OCD)

Most, but not all, people with OCD have both obsessions and compulsions. Contamination and pathological counting/checking are common themes, but not the only ones. Having obsessions only, with no associated compulsions, is sometimes referred to as "pure-O" OCD.

The diagnostic criteria for obsessive compulsive disorder are:

✦ *There is the presence of obsessions, compulsions, or both:*

• *Obsessions involve both of:*

▸ *Persistent, unwanted, involuntary, and intrusive thoughts/urges that cause marked distress*

Obsessions are usually "ego-dystonic", meaning they are not consistent with the individual's usual belief system. Instead, they are unwanted and push their way involuntarily into an individual's conscious awareness. While a "normal" person who is jokingly labelled as a "clean freak" may be preoccupied with cleanliness, those ideas may be consistent with their beliefs and desires, and they become satisfied when a certain level of cleanliness is reached. Obsessions, on the other hand, are not something that would be freely chosen by the person with OCD, and there is no way of fulfilling the obsessions in a satisfying, lasting way.

▸ *The person tries to suppress these thoughts/urges or neutralize them by acting out a compulsion*

In "pure-O" OCD, this would involve attempts at mentally suppressing the thoughts/urges rather than performing a compulsive behaviour.

• *Compulsions are defined by:*

▸ *Repetitive behaviours or mental activities that the individual feels they must rigidly perform in response to the obsessive thoughts/urges*

Someone with OCD may have the distorted belief that performing the compulsion in a highly specific way will allow for alleviation of their distress. While performing compulsions may in fact serve to lessen distress somewhat on a very temporary basis, overall these behaviours serve to further reinforce and propagate the OCD cycle. Breaking this cycle is a key goal of exposure and response prevention, a form of therapy commonly used for OCD.

▸ *While the behaviours are attempts to reduce distress or prevent negative events, there is no realistic way that they would actually accomplish that*

A compulsive ritual may involve performing a certain task exactly X number of times in the hopes of preventing outcome Y, despite there being no reasonable or plausible way that X and Y could actually be connected in that way.

✦ *The obsessions/compulsions take up at least an hour daily and "cause clinically significant distress or impairment in social, occupational, or other important areas of functioning."*

This criterion helps to distinguish illness from a "normal" person who may occasionally do some repetitive checking. It may be useful to get input from a significant other or family members to help determine the level of impact. In severe cases of OCD much of the day may be consumed by the obsessions and compulsions.

✦ *The symptoms are not due to the direct effects of a drug or medical condition, and are not better accounted for by another mental disorder.*

The level of insight into the illness varies amongst people with OCD. Sometimes the OCD-related beliefs will grow to delusional (i.e. psychotic) proportions.

Dysfunctional OCD beliefs may relate to perfectionism, inability to tolerate uncertainty, and a sense of need to control thoughts. Common themes for obsessions and compulsions include cleaning, orderliness, fear of harm, and the belief that certain thoughts are forbidden. Some people may fear that harm may result from discarding objects, leading to hoarding behaviours. There may be feelings of anxiety, panic, and disgust. Certain people or places may be avoided in an attempt to avoid contamination.

OCD occurs in just above 1% of the population, and is slightly more common in females than males. The average age of onset in the United States is 19.5 years old, with males typically developing symptoms earlier than females. In almost one quarter of males, the illness appears by age 10. Childhood abuse may increase the risk for developing OCD. OCD is associated with an increased risk for suicide.

Katie's Story (OCD)

Years ago, I was getting treated for panic disorder with agoraphobia. I panicked over a lot of thoughts, even leaving the house. At a time I was told that I had OCD tendencies, but never given a diagnosis of OCD. I didn't wash my hands extensively or need things in order before I left the house. Instead, I ruminated all day and would put myself in a panic over things.

When I was diagnosed with OCD, I said "oh great, I have graduated…" Seems like I have it all, panic with agoraphobia, OCD, PTSD, and major depression. I see a therapist who specializes in OCD and I go to a support group, but still question if I have it.

Some of my most frequent obsessions:

Sleep
In the past, I have obsessed about sleep. I still think about it, but don't compulse too much. After I had my daughter, I would not be able to sleep. The day or days after, I would obsess all

day about nightfall. Will I sleep? What if I don't sleep? I was afraid I forgot how to fall asleep. I would take bubble baths and do special routines (compulsions) hoping that they would take away my sleep problems. And they did, but it has also showed me that I need to do these things in order to sleep. And if they don't work, that makes my anxiety that much worse, until I get a few days of regular sleep and forget about it slowly.

Is there a God?

I wonder if there is a God. This causes much distress. When I was younger, I never questioned it. Then I ran into people who didn't believe. I then began to wonder how something can come from nothing. When people tell me they will pray for me or tell me to lean on God, I get triggered again.

When my dad passed away, I didn't feel him around me. At that time, I really began to question God and the afterlife. When my mom got sick with lung cancer, I thought "God will show himself and heal her here on this earth." That's all I wanted. I thought he was going to prove he was around. But my mother suffered a stroke and we had to put her in hospice. She passed away. I Google because I really want to believe.

Eating/Weight loss

Before my mom passed, I didn't have an appetite. I would force myself to eat, but really didn't want to eat. After she got sick and ultimately passed away, my appetite was so bad that I started losing weight. Someone mentioned to me that I had lost weight and "needed to eat." I told myself that something was wrong and that I must eat.

It bothered me that I didn't want to eat and I will get anxious when others eat, when I was hungry but didn't have the desire to eat... and when I had to eat. When I do eat, sometimes, I will throw up in my mouth (so as not to lose calories). I will swallow it back. I gag a lot.

I will do compulsions such as count calories to make sure that I am getting in enough calories. I will also avoid people, afraid they will say "you've lost weight," like so many others have.

I obsess if I am going to be able to work, what treatment I should be getting, if I will ever get better. I wonder what people think of me. Constant ruminations following by avoiding or looking for answers.

I'd say please pray for me, but "what if....?"

–Katie, *Let's Talk Anxiety Disorders and Depression*

❊ ❊ ❊

Body Dysmorphic Disorder

While many people with eating disorders experience some degree of body dysmorphia (perceiving the body in a way that is highly distorted from reality), there is also a distinct body dysmorphic disorder diagnosis that does not involve having an eating disorder.

The diagnostic criteria for body dysmorphic disorder are:

✦ *There is preoccupation with one's own defects/flaws, even though these flaws are minor, or even invisible, to others.*

> There is a major difference between what the affected individual sees and what others would see, and significant mental energy is devoted to thinking about perceived flaws.

✦ *There are repetitive checking/grooming behaviours or mental comparisons of the self to others as a result of the perceived flaws.*

> These repetitions consume a significant amount of time and go far beyond what would be considered reasonable for a "normal" person.

✦ *"The preoccupation causes clinically significant distress or impairment in social, occupational, or other areas of functioning."*

✦ *The symptoms are not better accounted for by an eating disorder.*

> It's common for individuals with eating disorders to have disturbed body image, but it is a core part of their eating disorder rather than a distinct disorder requiring a separate diagnosis. A separate diagnosis of body dysmorphic disorder would only be considered if the body dysmorphia occurred in such a way that it was not only within the confines of the eating disorder.

There is a subtype "with muscle dysmorphia", in which the individual (almost always male) is preoccupied with the belief that their body is not muscular enough.

Some people with body dysmorphia have a degree of insight into their condition, while others have distorted beliefs that become delusional in intensity. Most often, insight is poor, and 1/3 or more have delusional beliefs. Delusions may include the belief that others are noticing and mocking them.

Any body part can be the area of focus. The thoughts/preoccupations consume a significant amount of time, averaging 3-8 hours per day. The thoughts tend to be intrusive, unwanted, and hard to control. Like compulsions in OCD, the repetitive behaviours or mental comparisons are performed with a sense of necessity and do not bring about any real relief. Compulsive skin picking is common in an attempt to repair perceived flaws.

Individuals with body dysmorphia are prone to anxiety, social anxiety, depressed mood, and perfectionistic and neurotic traits. Self-esteem tends to be low, and the individual may feel ashamed because of both their perceived appearance and their disorder itself. It's common for people with body dysmorphia to seek out cosmetic treatments, including surgery. However, getting these procedures usually results in feeling even worse.

In the United States, about 2.4% of people experience body dysmorphic disorder. Rates are slightly higher in females than males, and the prevalence is lower outside the United States. The disorder is more commonly seen among people seeking dermatological services, cosmetic surgery, or maxillofacial surgery.

The average age of onset is 16-17 years old, with some symptoms often beginning around 12-13 years. There is an elevated risk of suicide in people with this disorder.

Trichotillomania and Other Body-Focused Repetitive Behaviour Disorders

Body-focused repetitive behaviour (BFRB) disorders involve compulsive behaviours that are acted out on the sufferer's own body. There are multiple forms of BFRB disorders. Trichotillomania involves hair pulling, excoriation disorder (dermatillomania) involves skin picking, and onychophagia involves nail-biting. The diagnostic criteria are similar regardless of the specific BFRB disorder, but the criteria for trichotillomania will be covered here as a representative example. Most people with trichotillomania also exhibit some other form(s) of body-focused repetitive behaviours.

The diagnostic criteria for trichotillomania are:

✦ *There is recurrent hair pulling leading to loss of hair.*

This may involve any part of the body, and the behavioural pattern may fluctuate over time. The scalp, eyebrows, and eyelashes are common locations for hair pulling. Hair loss may not be easily noticeable if the individual has been careful about widely distributing the sites of hair pulling across the body. Some people will try to hide their hair loss using makeup or head coverings.

✦ *There are repeated attempts to cut down on hair pulling or stop it altogether.*

This is quite similar to a diagnostic criterion for substance use disorders, where there have been multiple failed attempts to cut down.

✦ *"The hair pulling causes clinically significant distress or impairment in social, occupational, or other important areas of functioning."*

Distress can result from shame and a sense of loss of control. The shame may lead to avoidance of activities where other people would be present, which can significantly affect overall functioning.

The level of distress is important in differentiating the disorder from "normal". While hair pulling may not be common outside of trichotillomania, some degree of skin picking is a behaviour that's relatively common in people who don't have excoriation disorder. In "normal" skin picking, engaging in picking behaviour such as picking at scabs might actually feel somewhat satisfying, but in disordered skin picking the behaviour is more along the lines of an OCD compulsion, in that there may be a very brief sense of relief, but overall engaging in the behaviour increases the level of distress and reinforces the strength of the behavioural compulsion.

✦ *The symptoms are not due to a medical condition, including a skin condition, and are not better accounted for by another mental illness.*

There may be idiosyncratic patterns to the hair pulling, involving particular types of hair that are pulled and a particular manner of pulling it. Triggers may include anxiety or boredom. Hair pulling may be automatic, a conscious behaviour, or a mix of both. It's usually not experienced as painful. People may only engage in hair pulling if they are alone or around immediate family members, as they want to avoid the shame of being witnessed by outsiders.

The prevalence for trichotillomania is 1-2%, and it's about 10 times more common in females than males. The prevalence for excoriation (skin picking) disorder is similar, but the gender difference is not as large. Onset is most commonly during adolescence.

Ashley L Peterson

❅ ❅ ❅

Beckie's Story (Body-Focused Repetitive Behaviour Disorder)

I was diagnosed in 2015 with bipolar I with suicidal ideation and severe depression, an anxiety disorder, PTSD, and OCD. Part of my OCD extends to nail-biting, also known as onychophagia. This is a body-focused repetitive behaviour that involves the destruction of my fingernails.

Evidently, I've had this my entire life. I was always a nail biter, but not to the severity that it is now. I literally chew, gnaw, and rip the fingernails completely out, causing injury to myself. Even when there are no nails left, I'll continue biting and removing the skin. Infections are a daily thing. Also, when I'm doing this, I'm not even conscious of myself doing it.

The damage that I have done to myself is what my therapist calls self-harm. It stems from tension leading to distress. Family stress such as my sister's maltreatment of our elderly mother is a severe trigger for me. After one family incident, even though I already didn't have nails left to bite, whatever had been trying to grow back was ripped right out. Four fingers in one shot. Lots of blood followed, and the infections started right back up all over again.

To me, it's as if I'm on auto-pilot and to be frank, it's almost satisfying to me when I have done the damage. It's almost as if it's a soothing/calming sensation to bite and gnaw. It's like a baby sucking its thumb, a sense of self-soothing although it hurts like all hell.

This nail-biting is not only a behavioural problem, but the appearance of my nails is also hideous. It's embarrassing and I'm so ashamed of what my hands look like. I normally hide my hands when out in public, even with friends. I'm constantly questioned: "Why don't you just stop?" "They look horrible, don't they hurt you?"

If it were that easy, I would stop. And yes, they hurt like hell! I also feel guilty afterward, but it doesn't stop me from doing more and more damage.

The odd thing about this OCD type of behaviour is that this occurs when I'm actually relaxed while watching something on TV or a movie. I'm totally unaware that I have done anything until I realize my fingers are bleeding. I don't bite them all day, not even once during the day. It always takes place when I'm laying down in bed, watching something on Netflix. When I think I'm calmer, that's when this behaviour wreaks havoc. I guess in some weird way the stressors of the day or experience that took place affect me when I feel like I'm finished thinking about what had just happened, but the subconscious is still working overtime.

My therapist and I have developed a plan for cognitive behavioral Therapy (CBT), and I'm sincerely hoping that we can work through this.

— *Beckie, Beckie's Mental Mess*

Ashley L Peterson

Personality Disorders

Gathering a solid history is essential for diagnosing any sort of mental illness, but it's particularly important with personality disorders (PDs). Personality disorders are relatively consistent over time, unlike the maladaptive coping mechanisms that someone might fall back on while having an acute episode of a mood disorder or other illness. While a personality disorder diagnosis can sometimes be made after a single assessment, it should never be based solely on the way the individual is presenting cross-sectionally at that specific point in time. There needs to be a clear longitudinal pattern.

In the DSM-IV, personality disorders were categorized differently from other mental illnesses. Most mental disorders were on "axis I", while personality disorders and intellectual disabilities were on "axis II". The DSM-5 did away with this, but it retains the grouping of personality disorders into three clusters:

- **Cluster A (odd/eccentric)**: paranoid, schizoid, schizotypal
- **Cluster B (dramatic/emotional/erratic)**: antisocial, borderline, histrionic, narcissistic
- **Cluster C (anxious/fearful)**: avoidant, dependent, obsessive-compulsive

❄ ❄ ❄

General Personality Disorder Criteria

There are a number of general criteria that apply to all personality disorders. They are:

✦ There is "an enduring pattern of inner experience and behaviour that deviates markedly from the expectations of the individual's culture." This pattern shows up in at least 2 of the following areas:

Expected behaviour patterns may vary culturally. There should be clear, significant differences from what would culturally be considered "normal". The "enduring pattern" refers to patterns that are relatively consistent across the individual's adult life and in multiple different contexts. "Inner experience" captures subjective patterns of thoughts and emotions, while "behaviour" refers to what's outwardly observable.

- *Thinking*
- *Feeling*
- *Interpersonal functioning*
- *Impulse control*

Often personality disorders will affect all four of these aspects of an individual's experiences.

✦ *This pattern is inflexible, occurring across a wide range of different situations.*

This inflexible pattern means that it's difficult for the individual to adapt their approach to meet the demands of different contexts, even if the approach they've been using has not been serving them well. As a result, the same set of maladaptive strategies may be used again and again. Maladaptive coping strategies are likely to end up making the problem worse, whereas adaptive coping strategies contribute to managing or resolving the problem in a constructive way.

✦ *This pattern causes "clinically significant distress" or functional impairment.*

Some personality disorders aren't necessarily experienced as distressing for the individual with the PD, but there would still be an impairment in the individual's ability to function socially or in work/school contexts. Narcissistic personality disorder and antisocial personality disorder are examples of PDs that may end up being more distressing for close friends and family than for the person with the disorder.

✦ *The patterns has been long-standing since the teen years at least.*

Personality disorders should not be diagnosed in the teens without careful consideration, as people can and do "grow out of" maladaptive patterns. That being said, adults with personality disorders do begin demonstrating some symptoms in the earlier years of life, and personality disorders don't arise spontaneously in adulthood.

✦ *The pattern is not due to the direct effects of a drug or medical condition, and is not better accounted for by another mental disorder.*

Personality traits, of which we all have many, are "enduring patterns of perceiving, relating to, and thinking about the environment and oneself that are exhibited in a wide range of social and personal contexts." Personality disorders come about when certain traits are inflexible and not conducive to adaptive functioning. This inflexibility is key, and is often a major target of psychotherapy for personality disorders.

Diagnosis of a personality disorder requires an assessment of the individual's long-term functioning across multiple different contexts. Sometimes a diagnosis can be made following a single assessment if there is sufficient background information available, but it may take a longer period of time to arrive at a diagnosis. The diagnosis of a personality disorder is not appropriate when someone temporarily displays maladaptive coping strategies in response to a particular stressor, including an acute episode of another psychiatric disorder.

Personality disorders often emerge in adolescence. For someone to be diagnosed with a personality disorder before age 18, the symptoms must have been present for at least a year. Antisocial personality disorders can only diagnosed in those over 18.

✳ ✳ ✳

Borderline Personality Disorder (BPD)

Compared to other personality disorders, those with borderline personality disorder (BPD) are arguably the most likely to seek out help for their symptoms. The "mood swings" that are commonly associated with bipolar disorder are actually far more consistent with the rapid and sometimes drastic shifts in emotional state experienced by those with BPD.

In the previous edition of the World Health Organization's International Classification of Diseases (ICD), borderline personality disorder fell under the umbrella of emotionally unstable personality disorder (EUPD), which had impulsive and borderline subtypes. The current version, the ICD-11, has completely overhauled the diagnostic labels for personality disorders, and now the diagnosis is mild, moderate, or severe personality disorder, and this is followed by trait domain specifiers.

The term "borderline" originated in the field of psychoanalysis to describe patients who were thought to fall on the border between neurosis and psychosis. The diagnosis of borderline personality disorder was formally established with the publication of the DSM-III in 1980.

Dr. Marsha Linehan, the psychologist who developed dialectical behaviour therapy (DBT), proposed a biosocial model for the development of BPD. In this model, biological susceptibility to emotional sensitivity and impulsivity in combination with an invalidating environment and related social factors can lead to the development over time of maladaptive coping strategies characteristic of BPD.

While the diagnosis of BPD is associated with considerable stigma, some people will experience a sense of relief when they are diagnosed, as they may recognize much of themselves in the diagnostic criteria and realize that there's actually a name for the way they're feeling.

The diagnostic criteria for borderline personality disorder are:

✦ *There is "a pervasive pattern of instability in interpersonal relationships, self-image, and affects, and marked impulsivity, beginning by early adulthood and present in a variety of contexts", with at least 5 of the following:*

- *Frantic attempts to avoid abandonment, whether that abandonment is real or not*

    Even small hints of rejection may trigger this, including separations that are short-term or unavoidable. This can have profound impacts on self-image, and may be interpreted by the individual as a sign that they are fundamentally "bad" as a person. Perceived abandonment may trigger intense anger, impulsive actions, or suicidal behaviour in desperate attempts to cope. It may be difficult for the individual to tolerate being alone.

- Unstable relationships with others that are intense and fluctuate between extremes of seeing the other person as perfect or awful

    This is also known as "splitting". Someone may be on a pedestal for being supportive (sometimes referred to as being the "favourite person"), and then suddenly they are perceived as rejecting or neglecting the individual with BPD, and as a result they are thrust abruptly to the awful end of the spectrum.

- *An unstable sense of self*

    Self-image tends to be heavily influenced by external factors, which may lead to sudden changes in values, beliefs, and habits based on what's occurring around the person with BPD. This may involve temporarily taking on a notion of self that fits with whoever else is around at a given point in time.

- Impulsively engaging in reckless activities

This may include things like excessive spending, substance abuse, promiscuity, or unprotected sex in an attempt to cope with the distress and/or unmet needs they are experiencing.

- *Recurrent suicidal behaviour or self-harm*

  This includes suicidal gestures or threats. These behaviours are often triggered by threats of separation or rejection. They may also be associated with feeling forced to assume added responsibility. The rate of completed suicide amongst people with BPD is 8-10%. Self-harm, which is also known as non-suicidal self injury, may occur in an attempt to cope with dissociation or a feeling of being numb inside.

- *Unstable, hyper-reactive moods*

  These intense moods last between a few hours and a few days, and tend to occur in response to interpersonal stressors. There may be periods of anger, panic, or despair, while positive moods are uncommon. Mood is often highly influenced by stress, and Dr. Linehan's model suggests a neurobiological difficulty in regulating emotions.

- *Enduring feelings of emptiness*

  The individual may feel there is nothing substantial at their core. This may be felt mostly in an emotional sense, or it may be experienced as a visceral feeling.

- *Intense anger that is often difficult to control*

  This may present as verbal outbursts, which are often prompted by the belief of being neglected or abandoned by someone in a caring role. These periods of anger may be followed by shame and guilt, which further reinforces negative appraisals of the self.

- *Severe dissociative symptoms or short-term paranoia related to stressors*

  This may include micro-psychotic episodes. These symptoms are usually transient, lasting anywhere from a few minutes to a few hours. The triggering factor is often a belief that there's been abandonment by a carer, and symptoms may be eased by the belief that the carer is fully present once again. Possible psychotic symptoms include hallucinations, ideas of reference, and distorted body image.

✦ *The general criteria for a personality disorder are also met.*

The DSM-5 notes that "individuals with borderline personality disorder may have a pattern of undermining themselves at the moment a goal is about to be realized." People with BPD are more likely to have experienced physical/sexual abuse, neglect, or parental loss at an early age. They may have co-occurring mental health disorders such as mood disorders, substance use disorders, eating disorders, PTSD, or ADHD. BPD may also occur along with other personality disorders.

※ ※ ※

Wonderfull Creature's Story (BPD)

Hi, I'm a 26 year old female and I live with borderline personality disorder and the stigmas that come along with it. I am not a psychopath or someone who is out to manipulate. I feel emotions to the extreme and there is no in between – it's black and white. It hurts – not physically, but it hurts nonetheless, it hurts very deep down in my soul and I want the pain to go away. I would love to feel physical pain if this pain I am feeling would go away.

I either imagine or am abandoned by other people, so my relationship life is not what it could be. I either label people good or bad, and someone that is labeled good can become bad as simply as looking at me wrong – not that I want to do that, it just comes with the struggles of borderline personality disorder.

I'm either all the way having a crisis or all the way to the other side pretending and acting like everything is fine. I am currently seeing someone for my meds and I have a case manager who is licensed to do DBT, the number one treatment for someone with BPD. I struggle with feeling like I'm not real and don't know who I am, and sometimes I feel like I finally found who I am just to lose that again, so I constantly don't know where I fit into this world. I don't always feel like I have an identity at all.

Now this all affects my daily life in so many ways but some of the main parts are that I don't keep friends, and when I make friends, I think they are just going to leave me, so why make any when all the people I let in my life are just going to leave.

I don't currently work, which is partly why I can't make up my mind what I want to do, and also because of the fear of the unknown whether I can keep a stable job.

I feel so numb and empty. If I'm not feeling anger then I feel so numb to life and what is going on around me. I get extreme suicidal thoughts and sometimes it gets to the planning If I feel nothing, why continue living? This part is the worst to me, the constant feeling hurting my family with wanting to just die. I want to and hope to feel something other than this and anger. I want to feel the normal happy and sad. Truly I don't know if I ever will feel that again or go back to being my happy go lucky self.

This is my life. I hope people will understand more and the stigmas with this disorder will go away. We are not all scary people, just like people without borderline personality disorder aren't all scary people.

– *Wonderfull Creature, Mental Illness Worrior*

❋　❋　❋

Narcissistic Personality Disorder (NPD)

Narcissistic personality disorder (NPD) is seldom a diagnosis people seek treatment for, but given the prevalence of reports of psychological abuse by narcissists, it seemed worthwhile to include the diagnostic criteria here to provide some insight.

The diagnostic criteria for narcissistic personality disorder are:

✦ *There is "a pervasive pattern of grandiosity (in fantasy or behaviour), need for admiration, and lack of empathy, beginning by early adulthood and present in a variety of contexts", with at least five of the following:*

> As with any other personality disorder, there is a pattern that has been established prior to adulthood. Unlike the short periods of grandiosity that may occur during bipolar mania, there is a consistent pattern across time and situations.

- *There is an exaggerated sense of one's own importance*

> People with NPD tend to brag about their accomplishments, and at the same time minimize the accomplishments of others. They expect that others will share their opinions, and may be surprised when this is not the case.

- *Is preoccupied with a fantasy world of great personal success*

> This can include the view that they are entitled to some amazing success that is long overdue for them.

- *A belief of being special and unique, in a way that only high-status people would be able to properly appreciate*

Someone with NPD may believe that people they associate with are also of high abilities or status as an attempt to enhance their own idealized value by association. However, anyone who doesn't live up to expectations may be quickly devalued.

- **There is a need for high levels of admiration**

  The individual's underlying self-esteem is actually quite fragile, so getting constant favourable attention and praise from others is needed to prop up self-esteem.
  They will often fish for compliments, and may expect others to be jealous of their possessions or accomplishments.

- *There is an expectation of special treatment that is not merited*

  The person may respond with confusion or anger when they do not get things to which they feel entitled.

- *Exploits others to achieve their own goals*

  A sense of entitlement and lack of sensitivity can lead to exploitation of others, either intentionally or subconsciously. They tend to expect others around them to put in work/effort, while they offer nothing in return. Interpersonal relationships are maintained primarily for the purpose of enhancing self-esteem.

- *Displays no empathy*

  The individual generally does not recognize the needs or feelings of others, or if they do, it's seen as a reflection of others' weakness.

- *Envies others or believes they are envied by other people*

  They tend to believe that they are more deserving of success or valuable items than others.

- *Arrogant attitudes/actions*

✦ *The general criteria for a personality disorder are also met.*

Despite the grandiosity, at the core self-esteem is quite fragile, and as a result those with NPD ~~ily injured psychologically. This is sometimes referred to as "narcissistic injury," which ~~ge, or alternately with social withdrawal and a front of humility. An gative feedback can significantly affect occupational functioning.

Among those with NPD, 1/2 to 3/4 are male. Narcissistic traits are common among adolescents, but in most cases this won't develop into NPD.

Psychotic Disorders

Psychosis is not a diagnosis in and of itself; rather, it is a cluster of symptoms that can be experienced as part of a number of different mental illnesses. Some illnesses, such as schizophrenia, are considered primary psychotic disorders, in which psychosis is the defining feature of the illness. In mood disorders, psychotic symptoms may appear some of the time along with a worsening of other mood-related symptoms.

Psychosis may be precipitated by a number of drugs, both prescribed and illicit. In distinguishing between a primary psychotic illness and substance-induced psychosis, it's important to look back for patterns of how the psychotic symptoms and substance use have fluctuated over time. Sometimes symptoms of substance-induced psychosis will clear up relatively quickly once the person stops taking the substance, but this is not always the case. Crystal methamphetamine has a neurotoxic effect and can cause prolonged psychotic symptoms even with extended periods of non-use. Marijuana use in teenagers who are already susceptible can trigger the onset of schizophrenia. Steroids, whether prescribed or abused, can also trigger psychosis.

Some medical conditions may induce psychosis as well. Severe stressors can trigger a brief psychotic disorder, although that diagnosis isn't included in this book.

❋ ❋ ❋

Features of Psychosis

Delusions

Delusional beliefs are firmly fixed even when there is strong evidence to the contrary. Cultural or religious beliefs that are strongly held would not generally be considered delusional unless they represented a significant deviation from the cultural/religious norm and produced substantial distress or functional disruption. There are several common delusional themes:

> **~tory/paranoid**: There is a belief of being actively harmed/harassed or likely to be e way by others. This may involve things like being monitored, targeted or poisoned. People may engage in odd behaviours to try to protect

themselves from harmful external energy or substances; this is where the (unrealistic) stereotype of the tinfoil hat would come in.

- **Ideas of reference**: External things or actions are believed to be specifically directed at oneself. Examples are receiving special messages that no one else would pick up in a TV news broadcast, or believing that street signs are arranged in such a way that would only have significance to them.

- **Grandiose**: The individual believes they have special abilities or fame, or a connection to spiritual figures or well known public figures.

- **Erotomanic**: The individual believes that another person (often famous) is in love with them.

- **Somatic**: Unusual beliefs are harboured about things that are happening within the body.

- **Delusions of control**: The person believes that thoughts are being put into or taken out of their head (thought insertion or thought withdrawal), or that their thoughts are being broadcast for others to hear (thought broadcasting).

There are also some less common types of delusions, including Capgras delusions (believing that familiar people have been replaced by imposters), Fregoli syndrome (believing that an arbitrary person is someone familiar, despite clearly not being that person), and Cotard's syndrome (the belief that one's bodily organs have been changed in some bizarre way). These delusions are often highly distressing for the people experiencing them, and the distress tends to become even greater when they perceive that they're not believed by others.

Delusions may be broadly categorized as bizarre or non-bizarre. A bizarre delusion is entirely implausible, such as aliens stopping by and removing some of a person's internal organs during the night, while a non-bizarre delusion would be within the realm of possibility but highly unlikely. With the level of monitoring given current technology, concerns about being monitored by the CIA may have some basis in reality, but with a delusion the level of fixation and associated distress would be disproportionate.

It can sometimes be difficult for a clinician to determine certain statements are reality-based or not. Collateral information from other sources may be helpful with this. If that's not available, it can be useful to probe into the person's relationship with the belief. If someone actually has a relationship with someone famous, they're likely to be relatively nonchalant about it, but if it's a delusion they're likely to be highly preoccupied with that belief. What's most important, though, is whether the belief is impacting the person's ability to function.

Hallucinations

Hallucinations involve sounds, sights, touches, smells, or tastes that are not based in external environmental stimuli. Auditory hallucinations are the most common form, and these are often experienced as voices. The voices may be familiar or unfamiliar. Hallucinations are experienced as very real, but sometimes people have sufficient insight to recognize that what they're perceiving doesn't logically make sense given what's going on around them at that moment.

Hallucinatory-type experience that occur around the time of falling asleep (hypnagogic) or around the time of waking (hypnopompic) are not considered psychotic in nature. Some forms of hallucinatory experiences may be considered socially acceptable or even expected as a religious experience, and would not typically be considered psychotic. That being said, religious-themed hallucinations are fairly common for people experiencing psychosis. Some people believe they're hearing the voice of God while psychotic, and the effect of this on the psychotic individual tends to be quite different from what is experienced by most religious individuals who believe they're able to communicate with God.

Hallucinations aren't always disturbing. The voices can even be comforting, for example if someone believes spirit guides are present with them. The Hearing Voices Movement is an organization that aims to help people to reframe their voices as part of the normal spectrum of experience and approach them from a more positive perspective.

In mood disorders, hallucinations tend to be congruent with the person's mood. Alcoholics may experience a condition called hallucinosis, in which hallucinations are present while the person is otherwise mentally clear.

Disorganized thinking

Someone with disorganized thinking may move from one idea to another that is entirely unrelated, making it is difficult to ascertain a coherent meaning. Severe disorganization is sometimes described as "word salad", with words being tossed together in a completely meaningless way. There may also be "clang associations", connecting words based on a similar sound rather than meaning.

Catatonia and disorganized behaviour

Catatonia involves odd motor behaviours without normal reactivity to the environment. There are several forms of catatonia:

- **stupor**: complete unresponsiveness
- **rigidity**: maintaining a rigid posture

- **negativism:** active resistance to being moved
- **posturing:** assuming bizarre postures
- **excitement:** excessive purposeless motor activity

Disorganized behaviour can include talking or laughing to oneself, displaying a facial expression that's very inappropriate for the context, and wearing clothing that's highly inappropriate for the weather.

Negative symptoms

These represent deficits compared to normal functioning, and include flat affect (lack of emotional expressiveness), anhedonia (inability to feel pleasure), social withdrawal, and decreased production of speech ("alogia"). Amotivation, or avolition, is a reduced drive to pursue goal-directed activities. As a result of these symptoms, there may be poor grooming and hygiene and limited eye contact. Negative symptoms can have a profound impact on overall level of functioning.

Soft signs of psychosis

This isn't a diagnostic term, but it refers to certain non-specific symptoms that may hint at an underlying psychotic thought process. These include being guarded/suspicious, giving vague responses to questions, latency of response to questions, and intense or inappropriate facial expressions or eye contact. There may be other explanations aside from psychosis, but these kinds of changes can be red flags that something more might be going on underneath the surface.

Delusional Disorder

In delusion disorder, the delusional beliefs revolve around a central area of focus, and outside of that specific area normal functioning is generally maintained. Hallucinations are either absent or not prominent, and if they are present they relate to the central delusional theme, such as hearing persistent knocking related to a delusion of being harassed by neighbours.

The diagnostic criteria for delusional disorder are:

✦ *Delusions have been present for at least a month.*

This is substantially shorter than the 6 months of symptoms required for the diagnosis of schizophrenia.

✦ *The diagnostic criteria for schizophrenia have never been met.*

If the diagnostic criteria for schizophrenia had been met at some point in time, the diagnosis would be schizophrenia, not delusional disorder.

✦ *Outside of the impact of the delusions, functioning is maintained and behaviour is not overtly strange.*

While functioning is impacted in the area specific to the delusion, this is mostly compartmentalized and doesn't spill over into other areas of the person's life. For example, someone who had delusions about being persecuted by a neighbour may be able to function reasonably well when they are at work, but struggle at home.

✦ *If there have been manic or depressive episodes, they have been relatively short compared to the overall duration of the delusional periods.*

This helps to rule out a mood episode with psychotic features or schizoaffective disorder.

✦ *The symptoms are not better accounted for by the effects of a drug or other physical/mental disorder.*

In making the diagnosis, it's important to rule out other primary psychotic disorders, substance-induced psychosis, and mood disorders with psychotic features.

There are several subtypes of delusional disorder based on the nature of the delusions, which may be either bizarre or non-bizarre:

• **erotomanic:** The delusions centre around the belief that another person, often someone famous, is in love with them. Often persistent attempts will be made to contact this person.

• **grandiose:** The individual believes they have a special talent or knowledge.

• **jealous:** The person believes (without rational basis) that their significant other is unfaithful. They may identify "evidence" based on unreasonable inferences to support these beliefs.

- **persecutory**: This is the most common subtype, involving beliefs that there is some sort of conspiracy to harm them. The person may be quite litigious, persistently trying to pursue legal action against the individuals they hold responsible for the perceived harms.

- **somatic**: Delusional beliefs are focused on things that are happening in the body, e.g. that they are giving off an unpleasant smell, or that their skin is infested with insects.

While people with delusional disorders may be aware that others see their beliefs as irrational, they're seldom able to recognize this irrationality themselves. Often people will experience irritability or anger in response to others who don't believe them. They may go to great lengths to seek redress, such as engaging in litigation or sending large numbers of letters to the government or media outlets.

This illness is quite rare, affecting only around 0.2% of the population. Generally overall level of function is not impacted to the same extent as what is seen in other psychotic disorders. The psychosis tends to be quite compartmentalized, and unless the area of delusional focus comes up, others interacting with the individual with delusional disorder may have no idea that this person is mentally unwell.

✳ ✳ ✳

Schizophrenia

Schizophrenia is a highly stigmatized condition that the general population tends to have a very limited understanding of. The illness does not involve multiple personalities, and it has nothing whatsoever to do with psychopathy (a complete lack of empathy or remorse). By far the vast majority of people with schizophrenia are not violent. While some people whose symptoms are not well controlled may display overt behaviours, such as apparently talking to themselves, most people with schizophrenia do not exhibit obvious "crazy" behaviours most of the time.

There is a related diagnosis called schizophreniform disorder, which is used for people who meet the criteria for schizophrenia except for the criterion that requires six months of continuous symptoms. It is a temporary diagnosis that helps to prevent over-diagnosis of schizophrenia.

There are two broad categories of psychotic symptoms in schizophrenia, which were described in greater detail earlier in this chapter. Positive symptoms are psychotic experiences that would not "normally" be present when someone is well, including hallucinations and delusions. Negative symptoms represent deficits compared to what would "normally" be present, including lack of motivation, lack of interest/pleasure, social withdrawal, and lack of facial expression of emotion. While the positive symptoms may be most commonly recognized as being associated with schizophrenia, the negative symptoms often contribute the most to overall dysfunction.

In previous versions of the DSM, schizophrenia was broken down into subtypes, including paranoid and disorganized. The DSM-5 has done away with these subtypes, as it was thought that there wasn't a clear enough distinction amongst them to be useful clinically.

The long-term prognosis for schizophrenia is best when there is early intervention, as level of functioning steadily declines the more acute psychotic episodes a person has. Symptoms often emerge in the teens for males, or slightly later for females. While some changes in behaviour may be noticed by loved ones, it may take some time to fully recognize what is happening. The lack of insight that is often part of the illness can make it challenging to engage someone in treatment.

The diagnostic criteria for schizophrenia are:

✦ *Criterion A: There are 2 or more of the following for a significant portion of a 1-month period (or shorter if it is because the person responds to psychiatric treatment), with at least one of the first 3:*

> These symptoms are described further at the beginning of this chapter.

- *Delusions*

> While the exact content of the delusions may vary over time, often for a given individual there will be consistent themes that persist throughout the course of their illness. Some people may be very forthcoming about their delusions, while others may be much more guarded. People may become agitated when challenged about their delusional beliefs, and may try to keep their beliefs under wraps in order to avoid this.

- *Hallucinations*

> Auditory hallucinations are by far the most common. There may be multiple voices that converse or argue with one another, or there may be voices giving a running commentary on what the individual is doing. Often the voices will say derogatory things, but not always. The content the voices are talking about may be related to delusional themes. Some people experience command hallucinations, in which the voices tell them to do something. In some cases a suicide attempt will result from intolerable command hallucinations. In the very rare cases that people with schizophrenia do become violent, it may be in response to command auditory hallucinations to harm another person.

- *Disorganized speech*
- *Disorganized/catatonic behaviour*
- *Negative symptoms*

✦ *There is a marked decrease in social or occupational functioning.*

> Depending on where the individual is in the course of their illness, the impact on functioning can be profound. Cognitive symptoms can result in a significant functional decline, and avolition can contribute to social dysfunction. Starting treatment early on in the course of the illness can help to slow the progression of functional decline.

✦ *There have been continuous symptoms for at least 6 months, including at least 1 month of symptoms that fulfill criterion A.*

> Symptoms that meet criterion A but haven't been present for long enough to meet the 6-month criterion would typically be diagnosed as schizophreniform disorder, and then the diagnosis would then be changed to schizophrenia if/when the 6-month criterion was met. Schizophreniform disorder is a sort of placeholder to avoid jumping the gun and giving someone a serious diagnosis prematurely. There may be prodromal symptoms leading up to an active psychotic phase, or residual symptoms afterwards. This can include vague speech or odd ideas that do not have the strength of delusions. Negative symptoms may be most prominent during these times, and may be the first symptoms of illness to appear.

✦ *The symptoms are not better accounted for by schizoaffective disorder or a mood disorder.*

> Schizoaffective disorder involves mood episodes, and will be discussed later in this chapter. Mood disorders may involve psychotic symptoms during particularly severe mood episodes, but this would not warrant a diagnosis of schizophrenia.

✦ *The symptoms are not due to the direct effects of a drug of another medical condition.*

> Chronic substance abusers, particularly those who use crystal methamphetamine, can have ongoing psychotic symptoms even when they have stopped using, and it may be difficult to distinguish between drug-induced psychosis and a primary psychotic illness like schizophrenia. Crystal meth can have long-term neurotoxic effects, so psychotic symptoms may not abate even if an individual has an enforced period of clean time,

e.g. while in hospital. It is also possible that someone may have underlying schizophrenia with a substance-induced worsening of psychotic symptoms.

Cognitive deficits in schizophrenia can include problems with memory, language, processing speed, and executive functioning (higher-level cognitive tasks like problem-solving). These relate to changes in activity in the prefrontal cortex region of the brain. There may be difficulties with interpreting social cues. Abstract thinking may be impaired, and an individual may become quite literal (also referred to as "concrete") in their thinking. Testing for this may involve asking a person to interpret a proverb or similar idiomatic saying. For example, the saying "it ain't over 'til the fat lady sings" may be interpreted by someone with concrete thinking as an obese woman needing to sing a song in order for a task to be complete.

Often part of the illness is a lack of insight into the effects of the disorder, a symptom known as anosognosia. This can make people less likely to engage in psychiatric treatment, and they may actively resist treatment. For family members this can be an extremely challenging part of the illness to cope with.

By far the vast majority of people with schizophrenia are not violent, and they are more likely to harm themselves than others. The risk of physical aggression is highest in younger males with high levels of impulsivity, substance abusers, and people with a past history of violence and non-compliance with treatment.

Over 50% of people with schizophrenia are cigarette smokers. There has been some research suggesting that this may be in part an attempt to self-medicate for negative symptoms. Schizophrenia is associated with an increased risk of physical illness and shortened life expectancy, which is likely related to an interplay of factors including smoking, poor health maintenance behaviours, and the side effects of medications.

The age of onset is typically in the late teens to early 20s for males, and slightly older for females. Occasionally there will be late onset after age 40, and this happens more in females. Negative symptoms may be more prominent in males than females. Schizophrenia occurs in less than 1% of the population. Around 20% of people with schizophrenia attempt suicide at some point.

Meg's Story (Schizophrenia)

When I pass people on the sidewalk, I face away from them and avoid saying hello even if they say hi to me. To be polite and acknowledge them would be to let them suck my energy away, and I don't have much energy to spare. Engaging with people weakens and pollutes my energetic field, even if the people in question are being "nice" or "friendly."

I was ice skating with a friend of mine once, and she asked why I kept pulling away from her. Why did I need to keep three feet between us, she wondered? I hadn't even noticed I was doing it, but I explained about energetic pollution. She asked if I take medicines, and I said yes, to which she replied with her beliefs that our problems should be solved spiritually, not medically.

As lovely a theory as that is (and I'm being sarcastic here), there aren't enough antipsychotics in the pharmacy to keep me from feeling overwhelmed by people's energy. Whenever someone gives me a hard time, like a pharmacist who doesn't want to fill my prescription, or the drug company who doesn't want to give my drug prior authorization, I become filled with hostile ire until, at the very least, I've ruined that person's day as much as he or she has ruined mine. I wouldn't say I'm entitled, because I don't think anyone should have a hard time getting their prescription filled. But I do have a dark side that comes out whenever I feel deeply threatened.

A good friend of mine said that that other side of me has its own vocabulary and way of speaking. It creeped me out when she pointed that out, but she's right. My paranoid dark side is angry and unwilling to be compliant with anything unfair. But, just to be clear, I'm not violent. The incorrect assumption that schizophrenics are all violent and dangerous is offensive to me.

At heart, we aren't violent as much as we are deeply mistrustful (particularly within the confines of paranoid schizophrenia versus other schizophrenias). We have delusional beliefs about how the universe works, but at the heart of those beliefs is a fear or inability to face the depths of how atrocious human nature itself can be. It's easier to believe in Evil Spirits, for example, than it is to face the darkness that lies within humanity.

But the years I spent terrified of the Evil Spirits were horrible. They lurked all around me, plotting and scheming to ruin my life. They whispered of killing my dad, killing my dog, burning my house down, and disfiguring me. It took years to overcome those terrifying beliefs, and in the meantime, they slid out of hiding each night after the sun went down, not to disappear until sunrise.

The Evil Spirits were our spirit guides, who create bad things to happen in our lives on purpose for the sole purpose of forcing us to grow and mature. This sense of not having control over my life was terrifying, and in a deep corner of my mind, I feared that as soon as I overcame my fear of the Evil Spirits, something godawful would happen to ruin my life all over again. In other words, I was damned if I did, damned if I didn't.

These days, I live each day slowly and deliberately, waiting to see what the day will bring and dealing with it as well as I'm able. I don't have to work due to receiving governmental disability, which is a huge blessing. Being unemployed enables me to cope with life as it comes at my own pace, and it also fills me with admiration for anyone who's able to function at the workplace.

– Meg, Why does bad advice happen to good people?

❆ ❆ ❆

Schizoaffective Disorder

Schizoaffective disorder is essentially a combination of the symptoms for schizophrenia and a mood disorder (either bipolar or depression). It's not always easy to determine whether schizoaffective disorder or a mood disorder is the most appropriate diagnosis, but it comes down to establishing whether the illness is primarily psychosis-based or mood-based. Schizoaffective is considered a primary psychotic disorder rather than a mood disorder.

The diagnostic criteria for schizoaffective disorder are:

✦ *There is an uninterrupted period in which the diagnostic criteria for either a manic or depressive episode are met as well as criterion A for schizophrenia.*

Criterion A for schizophrenia, as described previously, includes the positive and negative symptoms of psychosis. The diagnostic criteria for both manic and depressive episodes are described fully in the chapters on bipolar disorder and depressive disorders. There is no difference between the diagnostic criteria for a manic/depressive episode in schizoaffective disorder and those for bipolar disorder and major depressive disorder. This criterion also establishes that the psychosis and the mood episodes are closely linked.

✦ *At some point, delusions or hallucinations have been present for at least 2 weeks outside of a manic episode.*

This is the key feature that differentiates schizoaffective from a mood disorder with psychotic features. In a mood disorder, the psychotic symptoms only occur in the context of a mood episode. In schizoaffective disorder it's the other way around; mood symptoms only occur in the context of psychosis. It requires careful history-taking by a clinician to establish this, and the diagnosis may end up changing depending on how the illness evolves over time.

✦ *Mood episode symptoms are present for most of the total period of illness.*

This criterion establishes that the mood component and the psychotic component are very closely intertwined.

✦ *The symptoms are not due to the direct effects of a drug or medical condition.*

Schizoaffective disorder may be described as bipolar type or depressive type depending on whether there has been a manic episode or only depressive episodes. As a broad generalization, the degree of impairment in social and occupational functioning in schizoaffective disorder is typically greater than in bipolar disorder but less than in schizophrenia, although of course this can vary from one individual to the next. Insight may be somewhat better in schizoaffective disorder versus schizophrenia.

The incidence of schizoaffective disorder is about 1/3 the rate of schizophrenia. It occurs more often in females, who are more likely to experience depressive rather than manic symptoms. The lifetime risk of suicide is around 5%. A family history of schizophrenia, schizoaffective disorder, or bipolar disorder increase the risk for developing schizoaffective disorder.

Noha Nova's Story
(Schizoaffective Disorder)

I first felt something had changed in my brain when I was 21 and in college. My classes suddenly seemed so much harder and I was struggling to understand content. My confusion spread to even casual conversations with friends and I became reluctant to venture out, preferring the safety of my room. Eventually I admitted to a psychologist that I thought something was wrong with my mind, which began the long process before my official diagnosis. I then spent almost 2 years working with my psychologist and psychiatrist treating my symptoms which at that point indicated major depressive disorder (a.k.a. depression), but there were some psychotic symptoms I was exhibiting as well. I was seeing faces in objects, hearing voices talking when nobody was around, and experiencing paranoia. Cognitively, I was having trouble expressing my thoughts because it felt like something was blocking my ability to do so. Processing words, both spoken and in writing, was also an issue. The cognitive decline I initially experienced was definitely my biggest sign that something was wrong because the psychotic symptoms are the hardest to admit to and talk about.

At 24 I had my first full blown psychotic break and spent a couple of weeks in a psych ward. It was here that I received my official diagnosis of schizoaffective disorder – a combination of schizophrenia with a mood disorder, either depression or bipolar disorder. My diagnosis was schizophrenia and depression. Until this point I never realized just how much having a title would help me process everything that was happening because I then had something to research and learn about.

The years following my diagnosis were spent trying to "fix" my mind and get back to the person I was before I fell ill. But in the past year and a half I have realized that, for me, recovery has meant accepting my illness and finding a way to live in spite of the limitations it imposes. I have had 2 psychotic breaks that have required hospitalization but any others have been manageable at home.

The main word I would use to try capture living with schizoaffective disorder is uncertainty. I have mentioned in my blog how I feel that I am straddling the fence separating sanity and insanity, sometimes leaning more towards one side than the other. It is hard to explain the experience of your mind telling you something is real but a part of you questions the validity of that belief. Hearing or seeing something that you've been told isn't there but that your ears and eyes tell you is! Medication has only helped me to a certain point but I have never experienced a total absence of symptoms due to medication. This is not to say finding the right combination is not useful because it most definitely is. I will just say that everyone is different and it is important to find what works for each individual. The worst part is having my description of my experiences ignored because of the false belief that someone with schizophrenia can't be rational. While it is true that at times what I talk about makes no sense, if one recognizes that I am speaking based on my reality then it isn't as absurd as it seems. The thing to remember is that while one is experiencing psychotic symptoms, simply telling them that their mind is making it up does not miraculously make them see what is real. Try and put yourself in their shoes rather than forcing them into yours.

There is still a lot of research to be done on schizoaffective disorder but there's definitely more information available now than there was when I first found out about it.

–*Noha Nova, Schizoaffective Disorder and My Life*

Somatic Symptom and Related Disorders

There are several diagnoses that fall under the category of somatic symptom-related disorders, and this chapter will cover two of them, somatic symptom disorder and illness anxiety disorder. Somatic symptom disorder, previously known in the DSM-IV as hypochondriasis, involves over-attributing importance to physical sensations. In illness anxiety disorder, there are either no or minimal physical symptoms.

DSM-5 diagnoses in this group that won't be described here include conversion disorder and factitious disorder imposed on self (or another). Factitious disorder imposed on self was formerly known as Munchausen syndrome, while factitious disorder imposed on another was known as Munchausen syndrome by proxy.

Somatic Symptom Disorder

The diagnostic criteria for somatic symptom disorder, previously known as hypochondriasis, are:

✦ *There is at least one physical symptom that leads to distress or a significant negative impact on daily functioning.*

> The physical symptoms have a significant impact on the individual, either in terms of mental distress or impaired functioning.

✦ *There are excessive thoughts/feelings/behaviours associated with the physical symptoms and the health issues it's believed they are related to, with the presence of at least one of:*

This criterion establishes the primary focus of this disorder as the problematic thoughts, feelings, and behaviours that arise in relation to the physical symptoms and the person's attribution of those symptoms.

- *Significance and persistent emphasis placed on the symptoms that is disproportionate to the actual physical symptoms themselves*

  A symptom that a "normal" person might dismiss as transient or insignificant would be cause for extreme concern to someone with this disorder. As a very simplistic example, routine tension headaches might be fixated on as an indication of a brain tumour.

- *Ongoing, elevated levels of anxiety in relation to the symptoms and their perceived significance*

  The degree of anxiety that is experienced is not in keeping with the nature of the physical symptoms themselves and what would be expected of a "normal" person experiencing the same symptoms.

- *An excessive amount of time and energy is spent on the symptoms and their perceived significance*

  The time and energy expended in relation to the symptoms goes well beyond what would "normally" be expected of someone experiencing those same symptoms. This energy is directed not only at the symptoms as they are experienced but also at worry over what the symptoms might mean.

✦ *There have been persistent symptoms, usually lasting for at least six months.*

  The specific symptoms that manifest may change over time, but this criterion only requires the presence of excessive anxiety around some type of symptoms in general that persists for an extended period.

The level of severity of the disorder may be specified as mild, moderate, or severe, depending on how many symptoms are present. Other specifiers that may be used are:

- **with predominant pain:** This is used when the symptoms experienced are mostly, although not always entirely, related to pain.

- **persistent**: The symptoms are severe, last for more than six months, and cause significant impairment.

To be diagnosed with somatic symptom disorder, there is no need to rule out an underlying medical condition. In fact, it's possible to simultaneously have a medical condition that accounts for the physical symptoms as well as a somatic disorder involving excessive preoccupation and distress related to the physical symptoms. This means that clinicians treating this disorder should avoid questioning the validity of the symptoms the patient is reporting and instead focus on the associated thoughts, feelings, and behaviours.

Somatic symptom disorder occurs in about 5-7% of the population, and is 10 times more common in females. Childhood neglect, sexual abuse, and substance use may increase the risk for this disorder. Typically people will present seeking medical care rather than mental health care.

❋ ❋ ❋

Illness Anxiety Disorder

Illness anxiety disorder is a new diagnosis in the DSM-5. The diagnostic criteria are:

✦ *There is a preoccupation with either currently having or potentially getting a serious illness.*

> While somatic symptom disorder is focused on currently having an illness, illness anxiety disorder can be focused on current illness or the belief that one might develop a serious illness at some point in the future.

✦ *Physical symptoms are either mild or not present at all. Even if there is some realistic risk for a condition, the preoccupation is clearly out of proportion to what would be expected.*

> While the individual should receive an appropriate medical assessment, this disorder is not closely tied to presently experiencing physical symptoms, unlike somatic symptom disorder. The distress arises not from any physical sensations that may be identified per se, but rather from anxiety around the underlying medical diagnosis believed to be responsible for those sensations.

✦ *There is significant anxiety surrounding the individual's personal health and health in general.*

This anxiety can be prompted by hearing about another person's health problem on the news. Reassurance usually does not ease the individual's anxiety. The illness anxiety can lead to a significant restriction in overall functional ability, and association with the identified illness can become an overwhelming part of the individual's identity.

✦ *There are repeated and excessive health-related behaviours such as checking, or high levels of avoidance of health care providers or facilities.*

Checking can involve examining the person's own body, including physical indicators like pulse, or spending hours researching a condition online.

✦ *The general preoccupation with illness has lasted for at least 6 months, although the specific illness concerns may have changed over time.*

This isn't a short-term scare caused by discovering something concerning in a magazine article. It becomes a pattern of thinking that endures over a period of months.

✦ *The preoccupation with illness is not better explained by another mental illness.*

Sometimes psychosis will cause people to become highly preoccupied with strange things they believe are going on in their bodies. Even if a person appeared to meet all of the other criteria for illness anxiety disorder, if psychosis is the diagnosis that best accounts for the symptoms, an additional illness anxiety disorder diagnosis wouldn't be appropriate.

There are two specifiers that may be used for illness anxiety disorder: care-seeking type and care-avoidant type.

When people with this disorder do access health care, they tend to seek medical rather than psychiatric care, and often express frustration with the inadequate care they believe that they've received. Interestingly, the DSM-5 remarks that "at times, these concerns may be justified, since physicians sometimes are dismissive or respond with frustration or hostility." It is equally true that people with valid health conditions receive inadequate care, so it wouldn't necessarily be an easy call to determine.

Even if a person has a medical condition, they may still have illness anxiety disorder in addition to that. Short-term difficulty coping with a medical illness may be diagnosed as an adjustment disorder, which is inherently self-limiting, and illness anxiety disorder would not be considered as a diagnosis unless the symptoms had been continuously present for 6 months or more.

Illness anxiety disorder differs from panic disorder in that the health anxiety in panic disorder relates primarily to symptoms experienced in the midst of panic attacks, whereas in illness anxiety disorder the health-related anxiety is more persistent and pervasive. Checking in illness anxiety is typically focused on monitoring for disease being present, whereas in OCD compulsive behaviours may result from obsessive thoughts about preventing a disease in the future.

❋ ❋ ❋

Katie's Story (Somatic Symptom-Related Disorder)

You feel physically bad, but you must keep going. No stopping for you. Your head feels tight and weak, and a little dizzy. Your equilibrium is off. But you must keep walking. Soon, you feel this weird feeling in your stomach that makes your body start to sweat, and heat engulfs your back. Is this the time that you are going to pass out? You feel bad. So bad. But you must keep going.

Why? Because they say it's all in your head. It's anxiety.

After getting up the nerve to go to the doctor, she says she is not sure what she can do for you, that she has run every test. You didn't even go to see her for that. You don't want tests run anyway. But she needs to know that your white blood cell count was high when it was taken a few weeks ago by someone else. She is rude to you, tells you that you need to get your anxiety under control.

You feel so bad… so sick.

You have blood drawn and your white blood count is still high. The doc gets irritated with you because you want to know the number. She says that they will test again in 3 months and that this might be your new normal. It could also be stress, as you have Googled this yourself. It can be anything from an infection, inflammation, stress… or leukemia.

You find yourself searching every day for leukemia. Really looking for reassurance that it is not what you have. However, your symptoms are growing. Your body has been aching for some time. You are sleeping more.

And you just feel bad, all the time.

If not leukemia, could this feeling of equilibrium and sweating be a heart problem? Your mother had an arrhythmia and had "spells" at times. Or could it be that you are going to have a seizure? The morning before your father had his first seizure (in front of you), he said that he felt weird.

You feel bad every day. There is always something, but you keep going. Again, not for you, but for others, because of their judgements. They say it's anxiety. You have now added health anxiety as a diagnosis. Now no one will take you seriously for anything that you have. You feel bad? Oh well, you need to come trucking along. Chin up, put that smile on. Get into work, act like all is okay. No one wants to hear it.

The pain is real. The symptoms are real. Nothing has happened yet... but... what about the next time? What if this is different? You search on Google, you look for reassurance from friends and family (but not so much because they are tired of it). You see a therapist. You suffer and you struggle every day to appear normal, when inside you feel like you are dying. Thoughts and real symptoms consume you.

This is what they call health anxiety.

–Katie, Let's Talk Anxiety Disorders and Depression

Ashley L Peterson

Substance Use Disorders

Substance use disorder is a broad umbrella term that covers addictive disorders involving various substances of abuse. While there are specific diagnostic criteria for each class of substances, they're all quite similar, so in this chapter the criteria for alcohol use disorder will be used as a representative example. Specific disorders mentioned in the DSM-5 relate to alcohol, caffeine, cannabis, hallucinogens, inhalants, opioids, sedatives/hypnotics/anxiolytics, stimulants, and tobacco.

A key element that differentiates a substance use disorder from "normal" substance use is continued use despite significant negative consequences. Circuitry changes occur in a region of the brain called the nucleus accumbens, which deals with pleasure and rewards. These changes endure beyond the initial detoxification period when someone stops using. Cravings may be triggered not only by exposure to the drug itself but also exposure to associated stimuli related to drug use, including paraphernalia and environments linked to drug use. As an example, for someone who smokes their drugs, seeing a pipe may trigger a burst of dopamine release in the nucleus accumbens in anticipation of the effect of the drug itself.

The time frame for the development of physiological tolerance to a substance varies depending on the individual as well as the substance consumed. Tolerance to certain effects of the substance may develop at a different rate compared to other physiological effects. This may be particularly concerning with opioids if the tolerance to the respiratory depressant effect (i.e. suppression of breathing) does not keep up with tolerance to other effects, as it can increase the likelihood of overdose.

Certain prescription medications are associated with withdrawal symptoms, but the presence of withdrawal symptoms alone is not considered sufficient to diagnose a substance use disorder. At the same time, people can develop addictions to prescription medications, but in that case there would be other symptoms of a substance use disorder present in addition to the withdrawal effects.

The severity of a substance use disorder is specified based on the number of symptom criteria that an individual meets. A mild disorder involves the presence of 2-3 symptoms, moderate is 4-5 symptoms, and severe is six or more symptoms. The severity may fluctuate over time.

This chapter also includes the diagnostic criteria for gambling disorder. This is a type of behavioural addiction, which is sometimes referred to as a process addiction. While there is no substance involved, the behaviour is associated with changes in the brain's reward centre, the nucleus accumbens. There is quite a bit of overlap between the diagnostic criteria for gambling disorder and the criteria for substance use disorders. Gambling disorder is currently the only behavioural addiction diagnosis listed in the DSM-5, but internet gaming disorder has been included as a diagnosis for further study and potential inclusion in a future edition of the DSM. Gaming disorder is already listed as a diagnosis in the ICD-11 diagnostic manual.

❈ ❈ ❈

Alcohol Use Disorder

The diagnostic criteria for alcohol use disorder are:

✦ *There is "a problematic pattern of alcohol use leading to clinically significant impairment or distress", with at least two of the following symptoms that occur in the space of a 12-month period:*

- *The consumption is in greater amounts or lasts longer than the user intended*

    This symptom represents a loss of control over how the substance is used.

- *The individual wants to or has tried to cut down but has not succeeded*

    The CAGE questionnaire is a 4-question screener for substance misuse that is often used in medical settings; the C is for whether the person has had thoughts that they should cut down. Like the previous criterion, this shows a lack of control over how the substance is used.

- *Significant time is devoted to obtaining, using, and/or recovering from alcohol*

    In severe addictions, almost all of a person's time may be spent in the process of obtaining funds, getting the substance, consuming it, and then recovering from the aftereffects of its use, including hangovers, before repeating the cycle again.

- *Cravings for alcohol*

    These cravings may be strong enough that they overwhelm all other thoughts.

- *Failing to meet personal and/or professional obligations due to alcohol use*

This can include frequently being late for work or missing it entirely, or skipping out on important family commitments, even though these commitments would normally be considered valuable.

- *Use continues even though it has resulted in significant interpersonal problems*

  This is often key in differentiating "normal" from disordered substance use. In addiction the use continues despite considerable negative consequences in the person's life. These interpersonal problems may be fuelled by the failure to meet commitments as covered in the previous criterion.

- *Major social, work, or leisure activities are sacrificed due to alcohol use*

  The individual may avoid important activities in order to focus on the substance use.

- *There is recurrent use even in situations where doing so could cause physical harm*

  An example of this would be drunk driving. The potential for serious harm is insufficient for the individual to step back from the behaviour.

- *Use continues even though the user is aware that it has caused persistent negative physical or psychological effects*

  This refers not just to the presence of negative effects from the alcohol use, but ongoing use despite awareness of these adverse effects.

- *Tolerance, as shown by either of:*

  Tolerance is a physiological process that occurs as the body becomes used to the regular presence of alcohol.

  - *Increasing amounts of alcohol are required in order to achieve the desired effect*

    As the body adapts to the presence of alcohol, a steadily increasing number of drinks is required to achieve a given level of intoxication.

  - *Using the same amount of alcohol is associated with a diminishing effect*

Tolerance is also seen with potentially addictive prescription drugs like benzodiazepines and opioids.

- *Withdrawal, as shown by either of:*

  ‣ *Presence of typical alcohol withdrawal symptoms*

    With alcohol these symptoms show up around 4-12 hours after the last use. Severe alcohol withdrawal can include seizures and delirium.

  ‣ *The use of alcohol or a similar substance with the aim of avoiding withdrawal*

    Benzodiazepines may be used to manage withdrawal effects in medically supervised withdrawal.

Alcoholism is associated with significant physical health consequences including stomach ulcers, liver cirrhosis, and pancreatitis. Neurocognitive impairment may occur, including Wernicke-Korsakoff syndrome, which affects memory. Alcohol use disorder is associated with an increased risk of suicide, and it can temporarily induce mood episodes.

The annual prevalence of alcohol use disorder in the United States is 8.5% among adults and 4.6% among adolescents aged 12-17. The disorder is more common in males than females..

Candace's Story (Alcohol Use Disorder)

I'm Candace and I am an alcoholic.

A program of recovery many are familiar with, Alcoholics Anonymous (AA), would have you introduce yourself as I just did. If you think about it, it is kind of like having academic initials behind your name, but different. I am not endorsing the program of AA because I am of the mental sorts they speak of that "will not or cannot stop drinking".

I have four years of sobriety.

My drinking was not because I wanted to fit in or follow the crowd, but rather a form of coping. My childhood was consumed with continuous belittling and verbal assassination that went on to become my inner voice. Relentless, negative self-talk battered me blue long after I had left my childhood home.

At the young age of 12, I got drunk. There had been many times prior to this occasion that I had drunk beer but this time was straight vodka and guts. Specific details elude me but I clearly remember walking home from my best friend's house and my parents coming home as I strolled down our private dirt road. It was pitch black and as I walked, I threw up. I somehow got away with it and from there I continued. Weekends were consumed with finding someone old enough to purchase the drinks and the rest was spent chugging it.

At the age of eighteen, I graduated from high school and moved into an apartment with a roommate. I landed a job that would begin my career as a bartender. I somehow completed three years of community college and a year and a half at a university before having my one and only child. At the time club drugs were washed down with alcohol but this second choice substance would prove to be my contender. At the age of 33 I would find myself medically detoxed eight times with inpatient rehabilitation stays and two mental institution vacations. It took me three years before I claimed my sobriety date and holding onto it varies from day to day.

– *Candace, Revenge of Eve*

❊ ❊ ❊

Gambling Disorder

Gambling disorder is the only behavioural addiction that is listed in the DSM-5. The diagnostic criteria for gambling disorder are:

✦ *There are persistent gambling behaviours that result in "clinically significant impairment or distress", with at least four of the following symptoms occurring within a 12-month period:*

• *Ever-increasing amounts of money gambled are required to achieve the desired level of excitement*

This is the behavioural equivalent of the tolerance that's seen in substance use disorders.

- *Attempts to cut down or stop gambling lead to feelings of restlessness or irritability*
- *Multiple failed attempts to control the amount of gambling or stop altogether*

  This inability to cut down is a classic symptom across addictive disorders.

- *Frequent preoccupation with thoughts of past or anticipated future gambling*

  This is one of the most commonly reported symptoms.

- *Gambling often occurs when the individual is feeling distressed in some way*

  Gambling is used as a maladaptive coping mechanism rather than a form of entertainment.

- *Monetary losses often lead to later attempts to make up for those losses or break even, also known as "chasing" the loss*

  This is one of the most commonly reported symptoms. Larger bets may be made and there may be increased risk-taking in an attempt to undo or cancel out the prior losses.

- *Lying is used to hide the extent of the gambling and any illegal behaviours that may be associated with it.*
- *Gambling leads to significant losses or near losses related to relationships, work, or school*

  This tends to occur in the most severe cases of the disorder.

- *Reliance on others to support them financially in dealing with significant gambling-related financial problems*

  This also tends to occur in the most severe cases of the disorder.

✦ *The gambling behaviour is not better accounted for by a manic episode.*

  Impulsive, risk-taking behaviour may occur as a symptom of mania, and this could take the form of excessive gambling. A diagnosis of gambling disorder would only be given if the person with bipolar disorder displayed problematic gambling behaviour on a consistent basis outside of manic episodes.

Gambling disorder may be specified as persistent or episodic. Episodic gambling disorder involves periods of gambling interspersed with periods of several months with no problematic gambling behaviour. The disorder may also be specified as mild (4-5 criteria met), moderate (6-7 criteria), or severe (8-9 criteria).

While gambling itself is a common behaviour, some individuals (less than 1% of the population) experience significant negative effects that spread into other areas of their lives as a result of problematic gambling behaviours. Gambling disorder diagnosis is based on the consequences of the problem gambling rather than the gambling frequency or dollar amounts lost. The disorder is more common in men than women, although females tend to progress from "normal" to disordered gambling more rapidly than men do. Females are more likely to have a concurrent mood or anxiety disorder. Gambling disorder is also associated with substance use disorders and antisocial personality disorder.

Gambling disorder tends to be associated with distorted thinking patterns like denial and an unreasonable sense of control over chance events. Most people with gambling disorder do not seek out treatment for their condition.

There are several personality characteristics that have been associated with gambling disorder, including impulsivity, competitiveness, being easily bored, and having a high need for others' approval. In some cases problem gambling may be associated with depressed mood, loneliness, and feelings of helplessness. Suicidal thinking and suicide attempts are not uncommon.

Trauma and Stressor-Related Disorders

In the DSM-5, posttraumatic stress disorder (PTSD) was moved from the category of anxiety disorders into a new category of trauma-related disorders.

In the ICD-11 diagnostic system, complex PTSD (c-PTSD) is considered a distinct diagnosis and involves repeated, ongoing trauma such as childhood abuse. In developing the DSM-5, the committee working on the trauma disorders chapter considered this but did not feel there was sufficient basis for a separate diagnosis. The DSM does not dismiss this type of trauma, but rightly or wrongly they consider it to fall under the general umbrella of PTSD. Ultimately, every individual's trauma reaction is entirely unique, and the nature of the traumatic event(s) does not necessarily dictate the nature of the trauma response.

The DSM-5 includes adjustment disorders in the same chapter as PTSD, but both the nature of symptoms and the course over time are very different. Other trauma and stress-related disorders that won't be described here include reactive attachment disorder and acute stress disorder.

❄ ❄ ❄

Posttraumatic Stress Disorder (PTSD)

While the first diagnostic criterion for PTSD refers to the traumatic event itself, overall the disorder is less about the event and more about the brain's ability to process it and integrate it in a coherent and contextualized manner into memory. Because of this, two people may experience the same event and only one of them may end up developing PTSD. An important part of therapy is processing the trauma memories so that they can be stored more adaptively in the brain.

The use of a disease model to conceptualize a person's reaction to trauma is not universally accepted, and has been criticized as an attempt to pathologize an understandable reaction to a traumatic event. Whether a medical model works for you or it doesn't, what is of utmost importance is supporting trauma victims in their journey towards healing, whatever path that may take. I've mentioned already the problems inherent in a system where insurance coverage is diagnostic code-based, and even if someone doesn't conceptualize their trauma reaction as pathological, having a diagnosis may be helpful in obtaining appropriate psychological supports.

When used properly, the diagnosis of PTSD is not intended to pass judgment on how well a person has or has not handled a traumatic event. Instead, it should recognize the profound impact that unprocessed or incompletely processed trauma can have on an individual's overall wellbeing and functioning. When that is not the case, it likely says more about the individual clinician doing the diagnosing than it does about the diagnosis of PTSD.

The diagnostic criteria for posttraumatic stress disorder are:

✦ *There is "exposure to actual or threatened death, serious injury, or sexual violence in one (or more) of the following ways":*
  • *Experiencing the event directly*

> While being exposed to emotional abuse is not explicitly included in this list, this type of abuse often includes threats of serious harm, whether explicit or implied, and as a result would meet this criterion. This criterion also covers medical trauma, such as waking up during surgery.

  • *Witnessing the event happening to another person*

> Exposure solely via the media wouldn't be sufficient to meet this criterion.

  • *Learning of a traumatic event that happened to a close friend or family member*

> Death due to natural causes would not count towards fulfilling this criterion.

  • *Repeated exposure to details of a traumatic event*

> Again, media exposure would not meet this criterion.

✦ *There are 1 or more <u>intrusive re-experiencing symptoms</u>:*
  • *Intrusive distressing memories*

> These memories are recurrent and involuntary, and often include sensory and emotional details.

- *Recurrent distressing dreams*

    These dreams may be a replaying of the traumatic event itself, or may involve themes associated with the trauma.

- *Flashbacks*

    Flashbacks occur when memories of past events are re-experienced as though they are happening in the present moment. They may involve various combinations of sensory, cognitive, and/or emotional elements from the original event. The level of connection to reality that is maintained during the flashbacks is variable.

- *Intense psychological or physiological distress with exposure to triggers*

    The triggers aren't necessarily inherently harmful themselves, but they activate the brain circuits associated with the trauma to set off mental alarm bells.

✦ *There are 1 or more <u>avoidance symptoms:</u>*
- *Efforts to avoid distressing trauma-related memories/thoughts/feelings*

    This symptom involves trying to avoid internal cues associated with the trauma. This can include attempts to distract oneself or to numb distressing internal experiences, such as through the use of substances.

- *Efforts to avoid external trauma cues*

    These avoidance efforts relate to cues in the external environment, such as avoiding certain situations or people that would trigger trauma-related distress.

✦ *There are 2 or more <u>symptoms related to negative changes in cognition and mood</u>:*

    Some of the symptoms from this cluster overlap with symptoms of depression. If a diagnosis of PTSD would better account for the symptoms, then an additional diagnosis of major depressive disorder would not be given.

- *Inability to remember important elements related to the trauma*

    Trauma memories are encoded in a disorganized manner, so elements of these memories can be difficult to access.

- *Persistent, often generalized negative beliefs about self/others/world*

These can take the form of absolutes, e.g. always/never, all/none, everyone/no one.

- *Distorted thinking that leads to self-blame for the trauma*

    This is a common symptom, and an important target for therapy.

- *Persistent negative emotions*

- *Markedly decreased interest in usual activities*

    This includes loss of interest in activities that are normally pleasurable.

- *Feeling detached from others*

    This sense of detachment can make PTSD feel very isolating.

- *Unable to feel positive emotions*

    This is similar to the anhedonia (inability to experience pleasure) that can occur with depression.

✦ *There are 2 or more <u>arousal symptoms</u>:*

    This doesn't refer to arousal in a sexual sense; rather, it is a persistent hypersensitivity and hyper-activation of the body's natural danger alert system. This occurs in response to triggers that aren't actually associated with present moment danger.

- *Irritability and anger*

    The irritability/anger are easily triggered in situations that would not "normally" produce such a response.

- *Reckless behaviour*

- *Hypervigilance*

    The hyperactivity and hypersensitivity of the brain's normal lookout system for danger means that there is an intense focus on looking for potential harm, and a tendency to misperceive non-dangerous stimuli as dangerous.

- *Startle very easily*

    This is sort of like a car alarm that's too sensitive, and is set off at the slightest touch. The startle response itself may also be quite strong.

- *Difficulties concentrating*

With so much cognitive energy focused on hypervigilance, there isn't a lot left over to concentrate on other things.

* *Disturbed sleep*

  This is made worse by the nightmares that can occur as part of the re-experiencing cluster of symptoms.

✦ *Symptoms from the four clusters have lasted at least one month.*

  This is an attempt to distinguish between a "normal" and a disordered response to a traumatic event(s). Obviously once the calendar month rolls over a person doesn't suddenly morph from "normal" to disordered, but after a month the more severe trauma-related symptoms would typically have abated in someone whose brain was able to process the trauma in an adaptive way. The one month marker was settled on as the point at which the "normal" healing trajectory and the PTSD trajectory start to clearly separate out.

✦ *The symptoms cause "clinically significant distress or impairment in social, occupational, or other important areas of functioning."*

✦ *The symptoms are not due to the direct effects of a drug or medical condition.*

PTSD may be specified as having dissociative symptoms if the symptoms include depersonalization or derealization. Depersonalization is a sense of being detached from oneself, and looking on as an outside observer. Derealization refers to a distortion of the surrounding environment such that it is experienced as unreal or dreamlike. Dissociation may be a useful coping strategy while traumatic events are occurring, but then it becomes maladaptive if it persists afterwards in an uncontrolled way.

The symptoms that predominate can vary widely from one individual to the next, so there is no "normal" PTSD presentation. Symptoms typically begin within 3 months of the traumatic event, but it may take years for the symptoms to reach the level required for a PTSD diagnosis. If it takes more than six months after the traumatic event for the diagnostic criteria to be met, the illness is specified as PTSD with delayed expression.

Female gender and younger age at the time of the traumatic event(s) increase the risk of developing PTSD. Around 80% of people with PTSD also meet the criteria for another mental illness diagnosis, often substance use disorders. PTSD is associated with an increased risk for suicide.

❄ ❄ ❄

Alexis Rose's Story (PTSD)

For the first 20 years of my life, I survived unrelenting physical, emotional, and sexual abuse and neglect at the hands of my caregivers and strangers. As an adult, I had worked hard to repress my memories. I had packaged them up into tightly sealed boxes and lived as if I had no past, no real history.

I had successfully managed to keep the lid on my past until the early morning hours in 2009 when my daughter was hit by a car while walking across the street to school. I stood in shock and was filled with overwhelming fear when they patched me into the ambulance to speak to my daughter as they rushed her to the hospital. When I hung up the phone, I felt like my mind had shattered into a million pieces, the sound of glass cascading down exposing the reality of my life.

Fairly quickly I found myself in a precarious state of mental health. All areas of my life suddenly became overwhelming and out of control. I felt as if I was falling into an abyss. I was often dissociated. I was losing big swathes of time, feeling like I was watching myself from behind or above, as if I was living in a movie.

I was experiencing horrific and confusing memories and flashbacks. I was waking up screaming from nightmares. When I wasn't dissociated, I was on high-alert and hypervigilant, afraid for my safety, thinking that at any moment something bad was going to happen. I couldn't discern if I was living in the present or past. My anxiety and fear felt insurmountable. I was in extreme mental and emotional pain.

Before I had learned distress-tolerance or developed a toolbox of coping skills to draw upon, I simply didn't know how to manage what was happening to me. I longed for the emotional pain to stop. I began to have thoughts of self-harm and was so fearful of what I may do, that I began to isolate myself in my bedroom for hours at a time. I also started to experience a myriad of physical ailments that manifested as fatigue, muscle pain, headaches, and general complaints of feeling sick all over.

My first two years of therapy, I was flooded with feelings and emotions. I would recall and process the trauma with my therapist during the session, and then cleave off what we had talked about when I walked out the door. It was just too painful to hold the memory, tolerate the emotional pain, and manage my symptoms.

There are still times when the skeleton hands of the past get the better of me and I need to manage symptoms of PTSD. I've learned to accept that I am going to get triggered and try to practice self-compassion. I'm mindful of my surroundings to help control my anxiety and the hypervigilance. Navigating my symptoms can at times feel exhausting and often leaves me with the feeling that I just don't belong anywhere.

I try my hardest to live in the present and have an incredible network of support to help keep me grounded and hopeful. I know that even though my PTSD can often feel debilitating, I have found a way to live a full and purposeful life.

– *Alexis Rose, Untangled*

�֎ �֎ ✖

Adjustment Disorders

While adjustment disorders and PTSD fall into the same broad group of trauma and stress-related disorders in the DSM-5, the two conditions are quite different. Adjustment disorders occur in response to a particular stressor that has impacted the individual's life, and the resulting stress response is disproportionate to the stressor.

The diagnostic criteria for adjustment disorders are:

✦ *Symptoms occur within three months after an identifiable stressor.*

> The stressor may be a single event or multiple incidents, or it may be something that occurs continuously. Regardless, there is a clear linkage in time to the onset of symptoms.

✦ *These symptoms are "clinically significant", with at least one of:*

> "Clinical significance" means that the symptoms are of a sufficient magnitude that they would go beyond what would be expected as part of "normal" experience to the point where they would be considered indicative of illness.

• *A level of distress that's disproportionate to the impact of the stressor in that particular context*

> This is highly subjective, but the idea is that the person's reaction should be more severe than what would "normally" be expected given the type of stressor and the other circumstances in the person's life. The disproportionality should be in

127

comparison to the expected response given the client's individual situation, not the clinician's arbitrary judgment.

- *"Significant impairment in social, occupational, or other important areas of functioning"*

    This also aims to differentiate between "normal" and pathological.

✦ *The symptoms can't be explained by another mental disorder or a worsening of a preexisting illness.*

    If someone had another mental illness, exposure to stress would most likely exacerbate that illness, and an adjustment disorder diagnosis likely wouldn't be appropriate.

✦ *The symptoms aren't a part of normal bereavement.*

    Again, this is highly subjective, but it's another attempt to distinguish "normal" from disordered.

✦ *Once the stressor and its resulting consequences are no longer present, the symptoms don't last for more than 6 months.*

    Obviously while the stressors are still present a clinician would be unable to predict this with certainty. Where it does come into play, though, is if the stressors have stopped and the individual is still having symptoms more than 6 months later. This could be an indication that there are other factors, such as another underlying illness, that need to be addressed.

Several specifiers may be added to the diagnosis of adjustment disorder:

- **with depressed mood:** the predominant symptoms include low mood, tearfulness, and hopelessness
- **with anxiety**: worry and anxiety are the most prominent symptoms
- **with mixed anxiety and depressed mood**
- **with disturbance of conduct**: behaviour disruption is the predominant feature
- **unspecified**: problematic stress reactions that don't fall into any of the above subtypes

If the diagnostic criteria for this disorder sound vague, that's because they are. Particularly if you look at the unspecified subtype, there aren't actually any specific mental or physical symptoms a person needs to be experiencing in order to be diagnosed. It's kind of a generic catchall label for people who are having significant difficulties coping with challenging life stressors. It is worth noting, though, that adjustment disorders have been linked to increased suicide risk, so it's certainly not something to dismiss out of hand.

Adjustment disorder is an easy target for arguments that the DSM pathologizes normal human experience. However, since a diagnosis of adjustment disorder does require a significant impact on overall functioning, receiving a diagnosis of adjustment disorder could potentially be useful in accessing supportive treatment. Having a diagnosis, even if it's so broad that it seems to include everything but the kitchen sink, can help to provide validation for people who are struggling. It may have the greatest potential usefulness in people who are struggling to cope with receiving a diagnosis of a serious medical condition by helping them to get some added short-term supports in place.

The Diagnosis Experience: Interviews Round #1

In the next three chapters, the contributors share their thoughts and experiences related to different aspects of mental illness. Each themed chapter is centred around two questions, and each question is answered by several contributors, each with a different diagnosis. The responses show a great deal of similarity in experience among the various illnesses.

This chapter focuses on the experience of getting diagnosed, and the responses illustrate how difficult a process this can be.

Getting Diagnosed

Question: What did it feel like when you were first diagnosed? Was it upsetting? Were you expecting it?

"The first time I ever saw a psychiatrist was when I was in hospital on a medical ward following a suicide attempt. I realized I had depression, but was prepared to do anything to prevent being transferred to the psych ward. I was still well enough to lie through my teeth, and I was knowledgeable enough to know what to say. I talked my way into a diagnosis of adjustment disorder. It would take me getting much sicker and another suicide attempt before I was finally diagnosed with depression."
– Ashley, major depressive disorder

"When I was first diagnosed I felt relief. Finally a name for what I was dealing with. Now we can make a plan to make me better. I was expecting the diagnosis because a friend of mine

that was bipolar told me that she was pretty sure I had bipolar and urged me to get a diagnosis. When she brought it up to me I was sort of in disbelief, yet is was also an 'ah-ha!' moment."
– Phyllis, bipolar II disorder

"I'd had mental issues for years. When the term 'schizophrenia' came up, I was shocked. I took to the internet and researched it, and the many ways I could relate were mind-blowing. I was twenty-eight years old at the time, and prior to that, doctors had bandied about many possibilities, none of which sounded quite as extreme as schizophrenia."
– Meg, schizophrenia

"I never had an official diagnosis of anorexia nervosa. I saw three counsellors in the 1970s who suspected I had an eating disorder, but that was not the focus of our sessions (they were family/marital counsellors my parents had been seeing), plus I went to great lengths to hide it from them. I feared a diagnosis because I assumed I would be forced to gain weight and alter the habits I'd formed, which I believed were good."
– Paula, anorexia nervosa

"Sitting in my therapist's office, watching her type into my chart DSM Code 300.6, I felt very surreal. Was this really happening? All my senses told me I was in fact awake, that this was not a dream – from the consistent temperature and set up of the office, to the computer itself, to the clothing being the same that I had put on this morning. I gently gripped the arm of my chair and nodded, taking a deep breath as quietly as I could. It was confirmed. I had been right.

My diagnosis was a long time coming and had a lot to do with my own willingness to advocate for treatment and being listened to. I had repeatedly presented concerns about being diagnosed incorrectly to a psychiatrist I had seen for years at that point, and then later upon reading about DPDR, I had asked three psychiatrists to look into the possibility, and now three therapists. The diagnosis was made after we had confirmed the presence of ADHD, treated depression, and after administering the Cambridge Depersonalization Scale. A minimum score for official diagnosis using this scale – the only known tool at this time for diagnosis of DPDR – is 113. I scored over 200.

It was a strange feeling of relief. There was a name for my kind of crazy, and someone professional was confirming that we had taken the necessary steps for treatment to make sure

that we could find it. I took the paper home and stared at it for a long time, unsure what it meant for my future. If it had taken this long to be diagnosed, how long would it take to get better?"
– Elle Rose, depersonalization/derealization disorder

"When I was diagnosed with PTSD my first question was, 'How could I have PTSD? I wasn't in a war.' I was diagnosed 11 years ago when PTSD wasn't really talked about, and I had no idea people that could develop it, unless they were in the military.

I went into major denial – I didn't want to believe it was true. If the definition of PTSD that my therapist was telling me was correct then the memories, flashbacks, and the other upsetting symptoms were because I had survived trauma. I was put in the position where I had to decide to face my past instead of trying to cleave it off. It took me a while to be able to accept my diagnosis. It did not come easy for me."
– Alexis Rose, PTSD

"I knew I had anxiety; I'd always experienced it, though it didn't have a name for a while. First came the 'generalized anxiety disorder' diagnosis but as time went on, the more I talked to a professional about how I felt in various situations, they told me that I also had 'social anxiety.' While I wasn't surprised in terms of the idea of it and what it meant, I just assumed that it was all GAD. I wasn't upset by any means; I more felt that it made sense outside of GAD."
– Autumn Skies Blog, social anxiety disorder

Being Undiagnosed/Misdiagnosed

Question: Did you go undiagnosed for a long time or get misdiagnosed before getting the correct diagnosis? What was that like?

"During my first hospitalization, I was misdiagnosed as having borderline personality traits. I was a 'difficult' patient, and 'difficult' patients were automatically deemed by this psychiatrist to have borderline personality disorder. Please keep your stigma out of my medical record."
– Ashley, major depressive disorder

"My initial diagnosis was severe clinical depression. This was in the mid 80's and bipolar really wasn't a hot topic, but depression was. And that is what was focused on, the depressive episodes. Since I have bipolar II, hypomania is a little less severe than mania, so no attention was paid to my hypomanic episodes."
– Phyllis, bipolar II disorder

"It was frustrating, but my issues over the years haven't always lined up neatly with one diagnosis. It's been hard for healthcare providers to separate my personal problems (such as the stress I experienced as a child and the extreme family drama I could never escape) from my innate mental illnesses."
– Meg, schizophrenia

"I have a complicated diagnosis story. When I was about twenty-two and had been depressed for several years, autism was suggested as a reason that I was so treatment-resistant, i.e. the depression was a consequence of the autism so treating just the depression wasn't helping. I was assessed and told that I had a lot of symptoms of autism, but not broken down over the right number of categories for a diagnosis (you have to have X number of symptoms across Y number of categories and I had a lot of symptoms but only in one or two categories). Then I was reassessed a year later and was told the same thing: lots of symptoms, but not in the right categories.

I tried to put it out of my mind, but it never went away. I had a psychiatrist and a therapist who both felt I was on the spectrum, but neither gave me a formal diagnosis. Some people with experience of autism who I knew personally or who read my mental health blog also felt that I sounded like I might be on the spectrum. I thought I might be on the spectrum after all, but there didn't really seem to be much I would gain from a formal diagnosis, so I left it. If I was on the spectrum, I seemed to be pretty high functioning, so there didn't seem much point in making a fuss.

All of this took place when I was too depressed to work, or at university. As I went into the world of work, I suddenly discovered that 'high functioning' can be very subjective or situational. I discovered that I was having problems at work because of poor executive function (difficulty multi-tasking, switching tasks, or making decisions), communication issues, problems functioning in noisy environments, and more. In one job my line manager complained that my work wasn't as good as she expected. Then the job description was changed to a more people-centric role. I decided not to accept the renewed contract I was being offered as I didn't think I could cope with the role especially as my line manager made clear that she agreed I would not cope. After that I spent three months working in an open-plan office which turned out to be unbearable and to my shame, my work here was poor. I just couldn't cope. Suddenly a formal autism diagnosis seemed to be vital, partly to get adjustments at work, but even more for my self-esteem, so that I didn't feel like a freak who had two degrees, but who couldn't hold down even an entry-level job.

An acquaintance on the spectrum told me about a charity offering free autism screenings. I went along, was screened, and was told there is an 80% chance that I'm on the spectrum. Because of that my GP referred me for another assessment. I'm currently sitting on an NHS (National Health Service) waiting list, hoping that my third assessment will be more positive than the previous two. I know more about autism now, I've done a lot of research, and am 90% sure I'm on the spectrum; if I'm not, then I feel there must be some other issue I don't know about that explains my behaviour. I've compiled a long list of my symptoms to take with me to the assessment which hopefully will help to make my case."
– Luftmentsch, autism spectrum disorder

"Basically, I diagnosed myself, and eventually I made myself stop so I wouldn't die. It was a little more complicated than this, and happened over a period of several months to a year, but that's the summary."
– Paula, anorexia nervosa

"I was misdiagnosed for a period of about six years, and it was hell. I believe issues with dissociation began much earlier in my life – but it wasn't until over a year after my suicide attempt that I began to seek treatment. Initially being diagnosed with dysthymia, then with borderline personality disorder and bipolar disorder, caused me to be put on a regime of mood stabilizers which uprooted not just my life but made my dissociation far worse than it already was to begin with. Some of this had to do with doctors not recognizing the emotional instability that ADHD can cause. Other parts had to do with doctors mistreating and overdiagnosing BPD, as well as the treatments for BPD targeting symptoms of the disorder rather than the traumas that so often cause it to develop.

I thoroughly researched BPD and found that it seemed strange that a psychiatrist could diagnose something so severe with just one ninety minute session. I did match a few of the criteria points, but most I did not – for example, while I had felt suicidal many times in my life, this had been in response to untreated depression and trauma. I had self harmed when I was younger, but this had been in response to trauma, depression, and the unregulated emotions of

ADHD. Sexism, it seems, played a far greater role in my treatment than critical thinking. Even when I saw doctors who were capable, they focused primarily on the depression, either downplaying the importance of dissociation and ADHD or ignoring both altogether as symptoms that would simply go away when the depression was treated. There are far too many psychiatrists who want treatment of the brain to be an easy, quick process, but the brain is a complex organ, and careful attention needs to be paid to its treatment in all cases.

When I began paying attention, asking questions, and doing my own research, I found that not only did I not match the criteria for BPD, there was a minimal chance I had bipolar disorder, and all my doctors had completely ignored the probable presence of PTSD or another trauma induced disorder. I began my quest to find a professional who would listen to my experiences and do some critical thinking of their own about my findings. It was a long, difficult process, and I'm still grieving the years of my life it took away from me."
– Elle Rose, depersonalization/derealization disorder

"I was extremely fortunate that I was diagnosed correctly, and a good treatment plan was developed by all three therapists that I have seen since being diagnosed with PTSD."
– Alexis Rose, PTSD

"This is difficult. I think it is now apparent that I had it from an early age, but as a very young child, it was defined as 'being shy' versus an anxiety disorder, so I think that would be classified as un- or misdiagnosed. I was able to socialize, but chose not to, even at an early age, I guess. Getting the diagnosis was really more like turning on a light switch. Stories from my childhood and other events throughout life started to make so much more sense once the diagnosis was there."
– Autumn Skies Blog, social anxiety disorder

Correcting Misinformation: Interviews Round #2

In this chapter the contributors speak to the ways in which misinformation about mental illness can adversely affect people who are living with a mental illness diagnosis.

Being Understood

Question: What's the one thing you most wish people understood about your diagnosis?

"I wish people understood that it is not something that I can be healed from. I will have it for the rest of my life. FOREVER. With medication, therapy, and good coping skills, I can manage it. But it is life-long."
– Phyllis, bipolar II disorder

"Schizophrenia can be associated with a distorted view of reality. Back when I'd try to function in the workplace, I wrote off my schizophrenic symptoms as being personal weaknesses I simply needed to overcome. For example, when I'd feel as if I was in a foreign country and culture-shocked by the white office walls, or when my coworkers would seem like furry woodlands creatures, I'd brush it off as my own immaturity. I want to raise awareness of how schizophrenia can actually manifest, in hopes that if anyone can relate, they can find peace and not stress so much."
– Meg, schizophrenia

"I wish people understood that it's a lifelong struggle. I have an eating disorder and always will have it. You can't look at me and say, 'Oh, you look normal, so there's no problem.' That's not how it works. My mind is not normal with respect to food and self-image."
– Paula, anorexia nervosa

"Bulimia and other eating disorders aren't just about weight, appearance, or clothes size, even though it started that way for me. It's not about vanity or egoism. It's about control, lack of confidence, self-sabotage; it's a method for coping and trying to comfort yourself while berating and hating yourself at the same time."
– Caz, bulimia nervosa

"I think the most frustrating thing I run into consistently is that people mislabel DPDR as an anxiety disorder. While anxiety does play a role, much in the same way the amygdala becomes overactive in the brain after a traumatic event, it is decidedly not an anxiety disorder. I do experience anxiety – I experience a wide range of emotions, in fact, and can even experience them rather intensely at times – I am disconnected from it. My life is like looking through a fog, or looking down at the world as I float away from it, and emotions are the weather in the sky outside my window. I can see them, I can go outside and feel the summer heat or the rain, but they aren't quite my own.

At times, DPDR can be terrifying. You can look into the mirror and think, 'Who is that?', or find that it seems your hands are hollow things without bones, that there is nothing inside your body but blackness. This does not make it an anxiety disorder. The severity of the dissociation is scary because your brain knows this isn't right, but the fear you feel is not causing the dissociation itself. The two are connected – but they are decidedly not the same."
– Elle Rose, depersonalization/derealization disorder

"What I wish people understood about ADD (or ADHD) is that it's not a lack of discipline of children that causes ADD or a character flaw of laziness or lack of self-discipline.

Just like any other mental illness, it's not the fault of the child (or adult). It's a combination of the way your brain works and environmental factors.

But there isn't just one thing I wish people understood about ADD. I also wish people realized that it's not just hyperactivity in boys.

Women are less likely to be diagnosed in childhood even though it's just as common for them to have an attention disorder. This is because there are different forms of ADD. Some have the inattention and the hyperactivity, while others (particularly females) may just have the inattention.

It affects everyone differently and if we can pass that message on, maybe more females will be diagnosed earlier in life and receive help too."
– Casey, ADHD

"I wish that people understood that thinking or saying to a person, 'just get over it' is an unrealistic and shaming message. PTSD is an extremely uncomfortable illness to navigate without the added burden of thinking I am not doing enough to get well."
– Alexis Rose, PTSD

"I am not *incapable* of socializing; I just prefer alone time or one-on-one time to large groups. I do want to be invited to events/occasions, even though I might say no depending on circumstances. It makes me feel better to be included; even if one thinks I might not attend. I might surprise you."
– Autumn Skies Blog, social anxiety disorder

Stereotypes

Question: What's the most annoying/frustrating/hurtful stereotype about your illness?

"It would definitely involve schizophrenics being violent and evil. We aren't serial killers, and we don't go looking for trouble!"
– Meg, schizophrenia

"The most annoying and hurtful thing is that people expect me to be super skinny right now. Well, I'm not. I'm slim to normal-sized, but this doesn't mean I'm cured. I still have an unhealthy relationship with food and with self-image – I feel like I 'should be' much thinner, though logically I know I'm fine. Emotionally, I feel I am a 'bad person' for being at a normal weight even to this day. And it permeates every other aspect of life, since so much of life and relationships involve eating."
– Paula, anorexia nervosa

"Stereotypes about eating disorders can be dangerous and incredibly insulting. One problem is with believing those with bulimia are, or should be, underweight. The majority of bulimics will actually be within the 'normal' BMI range. In general, pervasive stereotypes see anorexics as being weak and egotistical, binge eaters as overweight, disgusting, and lacking self-control, and bulimics as a mixture of the two."
– Caz, bulimia nervosa

"I think the worst thing about it is that trying to get diagnosed was just so difficult because 'well, that's rare'. At the same time, PTSD, a commonly accepted diagnosis, has a subset for persons with PTSD who experience severe depersonalization and derealization. Over and over I ran into doctors who were sorry I had been through so much trauma in my life and yet were unwilling to properly treat me for this trauma or listen to me concerning my dissociative symptoms. I do not believe DPDR is a rare disorder, but instead a disorder that is not well known or discussed nearly enough, even in professional circles. I feel that this applies to disorders based in trauma in general, especially when a woman is looking to be listened to and diagnosed."
– Elle Rose, depersonalization/derealization disorder

"I get angry when people insist that ADD is a made up disorder for kids who can't be controlled. There are so many people who deny mental illness because they haven't experienced it themselves and because of the stigma that was passed on by family.

Just because you don't understand something, doesn't mean it's not valid."
– Casey, ADHD

"The two most frustrating misconceptions about PTSD to me are: only soldiers develop PTSD, and that a person with PTSD is dangerous."
– Alexis Rose, PTSD

"Honestly that I 'wouldn't want to come anyway' I think is the thing that I hear that always hurts the most. If someone is having a gathering, instead of being asked 'I know how you feel about this, but I want you to come, if you are able' versus 'Well, I didn't think you'd want to come.' People think that social anxiety means we don't know how to, or don't want to socialize. Yes, we actually do know how and can be very good at it, but it just drains us much quicker."
– Autumn Skies Blog, social anxiety disorder

What Diagnosis Means for Recovery: Interviews Round #3

As previously mentioned, diagnoses can be most useful when they point the way towards treatment that works. In this chapter, the contributors will share the implications their diagnosis has had for their recovery.

Finding Treatment

Question: Has having a diagnosis helped you to find effective treatment? How so?

"Finding an effective treatment takes awhile. And even when you think you've got it, things change. Having the correct diagnosis for sure helps to find effective treatment."
- Phyllis, bipolar II disorder

"Yes, and the diagnosis opened my eyes to a lot of issues I've always brushed off. I was able to work with a great psychiatrist who has helped me adjust my meds into the ideal combination, which we still monitor every few months."
– Meg, schizophrenia

"My 'effective treatment' was to stop starving myself to death, which I accomplished on my own. As far as accepting myself at a slim to normal weight, that has not happened. I still secretly (or not so secretly) am thrilled every time my weight drops for whatever reason."
– Paula, anorexia nervosa

"I don't know that I've found effective treatment just yet, but I have developed many coping mechanisms I can use on my own to try and help handle the ever changing severity of the disorder. For example, I have 'You are real' written on my makeup mirror. I take polaroid photographs and go through them when I am feeling particularly dreamlike. I have a box of letters and notes I've been sent over the years that I reread to try and reassure myself that these people are real and I am real to them. When things are particularly bad, I try and tell myself, 'You are not going mad, you have a disorder. You have a disorder. This is the disorder acting up.' When that doesn't work, I ask the people around me to distract me, I find a funny TV show, or I straight up ask them if we're awake. Simply admitting it's happening – that takes away some of its power over me. Currently, though, there is not an agreed upon treatment methodology for DPDR, as there is little study of the disorder itself."
– Elle Rose, depersonalization/derealization disorder

"Being diagnosed correctly has been paramount in finding effective treatment. There are many therapeutic options that are available for people who live with PTSD. I have tried a few different modalities until I found what worked best for me. I know what works well for one person may not work for another. I've found that talk therapy, mindfulness, writing, yoga, and dance are all equally important for both treating and managing my symptoms."
– Alexis Rose, PTSD

"I wouldn't say it's helped in terms of treatment, but what it has done is help me understand parts of my past, why I sometimes act the way I do, why crowds affect me the way they do, and in terms of just being overall more aware of myself."
– Autumn Skies Blog, social anxiety disorder

Recovery

Question: What does/would recovery mean for you with respect to your illness? Would it necessarily mean being symptom-free?

"I think recovery means different things to different people. I used to hate the term. I'm not an alcoholic or drug addict. But treatment is a sort of recovery, even if there is no end in sight. In the beginning I thought recovery means you can come to the final destination of

being recovered. I now understand that for me, as far as I believe, that is not the case. I will forever be in 'recovery', but I really prefer the term 'treatment'. You will never 'recover' from a mental illness. You will always be in treatment though."
— Phyllis, bipolar II disorder

"No, it would not involve being symptom-free, because in my case, my mental illnesses are so wholly ingrained into both my personality and my life experiences that it would be impossible to eradicate the symptoms. I feel as if I am, indeed, in recovery now, and that's a great feeling. I problem solve whenever any mental or emotional issue arises, and I have supportive people to turn to. I've accepted my mental illnesses as being part of who I am, and I strive to live in a way that's as productive and fulfilling as possible."
— Meg, schizophrenia

"There is no treatment for autism, but my autism has an impact on my other mental health issues, particularly depression and social anxiety. I don't think I'm ever going to be permanently symptom-free from those. I think if I can learn to manage the autism and find an autism-friendly job, then hopefully that would boost my self-esteem and help ease the depression and some of the social anxiety."
— Luftmentsch, autism spectrum disorder

"Full recovery for me would mean to accept myself as a physically flawed human who is worthy of love regardless of her looks or size. I have never truly believed that and most likely will not, given my age (late 50s)."
— Paula, anorexia nervosa

"Honestly, I'm not sure. Though the DSM-5 and other sources report that many sufferers improve without intervention, and there are many people who say they have recovered online, I find that many also say that they have simply found ways of handling and easing their symptoms and the stress the symptoms cause. Because there is such poor study of the disorder at this time as well as no agreed upon treatment methodology, there is little public information about what recovery from the disorder actually looks like.

Mild dissociation isn't even so bad – it can help you get engaged in a good book or movie, or let you float around during a nature walk. The distressing thing is when it doesn't go away. I have been dissociating at least mildly since childhood here and there, and now that it won't shut off after years of more severe trauma, I ask myself 1) if it ever will after what I've been through and 2) if I truly want it to. As much as I do not like living in a constant dream state, or feeling like I'm losing my mind, my brain is trying to protect me from continued suffering. DPDR is a different kind of suffering, yes – but I have to wonder if it's really the worst thing that could happen, or if I'm making too big a deal of the disorder altogether."
– Elle Rose, depersonalization/derealization disorder

"For those with mental illness or other chronic illnesses, we'll never be cured or completely symptom-free. For me, recovery from ADD means being able to finish everyday tasks without my brain fighting against me the whole time. I just want the ability to fight back, instead of giving in to distractions.

I don't consider all my symptoms of ADD necessarily bad. Of course, it's affected my life in big ways when it comes to education and even work.

On the bright side, hyper-fixation helps me focus on what I love, including writing. I put in all my effort and create the best that I can create. It's also a distraction from depression, believe it or not. When I'm working on something I love, I'm doing something that makes me happy.

But I know I'll always be fighting. As long as I have a fighting chance, I'm happy."
– Casey, ADHD

"When I look back on my life, especially how far I've come the past 11 years, I am astonished at the difference. I was once completely debilitated by flashbacks, triggers, hypervigilance, and almost total mistrust in the world. With a lot of hard work, therapy, acceptance, and understanding my illness, I have learned to live, not just survive. I don't know if I will always have symptoms that I need to manage, but continued growth and change to me is a life-long pursuit and all part of the recovery process."
– Alexis Rose, PTSD

"Recovery, in my opinion, would mean more that I am better able to manage symptoms while in various events. I'm not sure one can really be 'cured' in terms of a life-long disorder, or at least maybe not fully, but being able to control and manage it, I feel like that is what recovery would be. I'm doing well with it, though with everything, there will be good days and bad."
– Autumn Skies Blog, social anxiety disorder

The Evolving Nature of Diagnosis

Diagnosis isn't necessarily static. As symptoms change over the course of an individual's mental health experience, the diagnosis that best fits the pattern of symptoms may change. The initial diagnosis may not have been wrong wrong, per se; it would simply have been based on the information that was available at the time. When certain symptoms are shared by more than one diagnosis, it can take some time to determine which diagnosis is the best fit.

The answers given to the clinician during an assessment can also impact the accuracy of an initial diagnosis. When I was briefly hospitalized on a medical unit after my first suicide attempt, I had a strong desire to avoid being admitted to psychiatry. As a result, I only gave the consulting psychiatrist a few crumbs of information, and essentially talked my way into a diagnosis of adjustment disorder. The diagnosis was changed to major depressive disorder not too long afterwards, not because my actual illness changed, but because I had become ill enough that I was no longer able to mask what I was experiencing.

Often people's symptoms don't easily fit into neat and tidy boxes, making it difficult to tease out what exactly is causing what. Someone with depression may have symptoms of anxiety and be diagnosed with an anxiety disorder, but over time it may become clear that the anxiety symptoms really only occur in the context of depressive episodes, so a diagnosis of major depressive disorder with anxious features may be a better fit.

If the diagnosis changes, that doesn't mean that the person changes; it's still the exact same person with the exact same symptoms. A diagnosis is a fallible human construct, and it does not define who a person is, although individual identity can be heavily influenced by one's personal illness experience. At the same time, a diagnostic label can be a powerful way to connect with others who share the same label and therefore share similar experiences. Within a given diagnostic label, there are many different potential combinations of symptoms, so two people with the same illness may have as many differences as similarities.

If you've been diagnosed with a certain illness and you don't agree with the diagnosis, it's okay to question your health care provider, but be smart about it. Ask them to break it down into symptoms that they see or don't see. Tell them what it is about your experience that you think their diagnosis doesn't capture, and how you think it mistakenly represents what you are going through. It shouldn't have to be a matter of you squaring off against them. If you're feeling dismissed, try bringing someone with you. Come prepared with a list of diagnostic criteria, and try to use that as focal point rather than challenging the clinician's judgement, since a defensive reaction is unlikely to end up being helpful for you.

Sometimes there can be a common focus even if there is some disagreement on a diagnosis. This brings to mind a former patient of mine who had schizophrenia. Because of the illness he had no insight into the psychotic element of his condition, but he recognized the negative symptoms of his illness and interpreted them as depression. Despite our disagreement on the diagnosis, we were able to meet him where he was and frame the treatment strategies as being beneficial for what he identified as depression (which they were). He ended up doing really well with treatment.

A diagnosis can be restricting or empowering, depending on how you look at it and whether it feels right to you or not. If it can help point the way toward effective treatment, then it's doing exactly what it's supposed to do. If it helps you to connect with a community of people on a similar journey, then that can be a really good step towards taking ownership of your illness and how it fits into your identity. Ultimately, what matters far more than a diagnostic label is finding a way to live the best life possible given the hand that's been dealt.

Contributor Biographies

Alexis Rose (PTSD)
Alexis Rose is an experienced speaker, writer, author, and mental health blogger. She has written several inspirational books, including her memoir, Untangled, A Story of Courage, Resilience, and Triumph, and If I Could Tell You How It Feels, which is a series of essays and poems about living authentically with PTSD. After surviving a horrific past, Alexis has chosen to heal, grow, thrive and use her experience to be of service to others who struggle with PTSD. Contact Alexis at atribeuntangled@gmail.com and follow her blog at atribeuntangled.com.

Alice Franklin (Tourette's)
Alice Franklin is a mental health blogger at how-to-have-tourettes-syndrome.com.

Autumn Skies Blog (social anxiety disorder)
You can find Autumn Skies Blog at autumnskiesblog.wordpress.com.

Beckie (body focused repetitive behaviour disorder)
Beckie is a mental health blogger at beckiesmentalmess.com.

Candace (alcohol use disorder)
Candace is a mental health blogger at revengeofeve.com.

Casey Elizabeth Dennis (ADHD)
Casey is a mental health blogger at bipolarbrat.wordpress.com.

Caz (bulimia nervosa)
Caz is a tea drinker, over-thinker and chronic illness advocate who runs the blog invisiblyme.com.

Christina (generalized anxiety disorder)
Christina is a mental health blogger and writes about self love, feminism and poetry too. My blog is seaofwordsx.wordpress.com and you can also find me on Instagram @seaofwordsblog.

Elle Rose (depersonalization/derealization disorder)
Elle Rose is a mental health blogger at secretladyspider.wordpress.com.

Johnzelle Anderson (panic disorder)
Johnzelle Anderson is a licensed professional counselor in Richmond, Virginia. He is the owner of Panoramic Counseling, a mental health therapy practice. He publishes weekly mental articles at PanoramicCounseling.com.

Katie Dale (bipolar I disorder)
Katie Dale is the mind behind BipolarBrave.com and GAMEPLAN: Mental Health Resource Guide. She enjoys her long runs and long naps to keep her bipolar in remission and resides in central Missouri with her husband and cat. You can follow her activity on Instagram @bipolarbraveblog and Facebook and Twitter @katierdale.

Katie (OCD, somatic symptom-related disorder)
Katie is a mental health blogger at letstalkanxietyanddepression540391349.wordpress.com.

Luftmentsch (autism spectrum disorder)
Luftmentsch is a mental health blogger at visionofthenight.wordpress.com.

Meg Kimball (schizophrenia)
Meg is a mental health blogger at whenbadadvicehappens.wordpress.com.

Noha Nova (schizoaffective disorder)
Noha Nova is a mental health blogger at ramblingsofaschizomind.wordpress.com.

Paula Light (anorexia nervosa)
Paula lives with her cat, Gatsby, in Orange County, California. She has several books of poetry available on Amazon, and she also writes romance as Anna Fondant. She's the proud mom of two successful adult daughters, and she's a grand mommy too. Her blog is lightmotifs.wordpress.com

Phyllis Engle (bipolar II disorder)
Phyllis is a mental health blogger at colormebipolar.wordpress.com.

Wonderfull Creature (borderline personality disorder)
Wonderfull Creature is a mental health blogger at emotionalillnessworrior.wordpress.com.

Ashley L Peterson

Author Biography

Ashley's first career was as a pharmacist, but she chose to give that up to become a nurse. While completing her nursing degree she realized that mental health deeply resonated with her, and she has worked in the field for her entire 15 year career in hospital, community, and outreach settings.

She was first diagnosed with depression in 2007, and since then she has been passionate about speaking up to challenge the stigma around mental illness. She completed a Master of Psychiatric Nursing degree despite two hospitalizations while she was in grad school.

She is the creator of the blog Mental Health @ Home, where she talks candidly about all things mental health-related. You can find the blog at mentalhealthathome.org.

This is Ashley's second book; her first was Psych Meds Made Simple: How & Why They Do What They Do.

Ashley lives in Vancouver, Canada, with her pet guinea pigs.

Made in the USA
Coppell, TX
15 July 2021

59008249R00094